D0054585

"People don't take advantage of me,"

Mark Fenwick said angrily. "Especially not a grasping little typist like you, Miss Shaw. Didn't you think you'd be out of your depth?"

"You've got it wrong." Sara stumbled over the words. "I never thought about anything like that. I can't believe you'd be interested in a girl like me. Not—not romantically."

"What other way would I be interested in you? Maybe I wouldn't have taken you out if you didn't have a pretty face and enticing figure, but that's as far as it went, and a lot further than I intended to go. Or are you disappointed that I didn't ask you to sleep with me?"

Resentment drowned out caution. "You are despicable!" Sara flared. Furiously he jerked her to him and his lips came down on hers.

Other titles by
MARGARET PARGETER
IN HARLEQUIN ROMANCES

Other titles by
MARGARET PARGETER
IN HARLEQUIN PRESENTS

Many of these titles are available at your local bookseller
or through the Harlequin Reader Service.

For a free catalogue listing all available Harlequin Romances,
send your name and address to:

HARLEQUIN READER SERVICE,
M.P.O. Box 707, Niagara Falls, N.Y. 14302
Canadian address: Stratford, Ontario, Canada N5A 6W2

or use coupon at back of book.

Only You

by

MARGARET PARGETER

Harlequin Books

TORONTO • LONDON • NEW YORK • AMSTERDAM
SYDNEY • HAMBURG • PARIS

Original hardcover edition published in 1979
by Mills & Boon Limited

ISBN 0-373-02284-0

Harlequin edition published September 1979

Copyright © 1979 by Margaret Pargeter.
Philippine copyright 1979. Australian copyright 1979.

All rights reserved. Except for use in any review, the reproduction or utilization of
this work in whole or in part in any form by any electronic, mechanical or other
means, now known or hereafter invented, including xerography, photocopying
and recording, or in any information storage or retrieval system, is forbidden
without the permission of the publisher. All the characters in this book have no
existence outside the imagination of the author and have no relation whatsoever
to anyone bearing the same name or names. They are not even distantly
inspired by any individual known or unknown to the author, and all the incidents
are pure invention.

The Harlequin trademark, consisting of the word HARLEQUIN and the portrayal
of a Harlequin, is registered in the United States Patent Office and in the Canada
Trade Marks Office.

Printed in U.S.A.

CHAPTER ONE

SARA SHAW'S clear young voice shook, something she couldn't remember happening for a long time, and her eyes darkened. 'I wish you had given me some warning of this, Mr Dent. It doesn't seem quite fair to spring such news on anyone so abruptly.'

George Dent eyed his capable young secretary with a slightly surprised lift of his bushy brows. Everything in the latter stages of the take-over bid had gone smoothly. Sir David and his board of directors hadn't quibbled over details half as much as he had expected. This was undoubtedly due to the fact that Sir David's managing director, Mark Fenwick, happened to be a man with a brilliant brain, appearing to be fully conversant with every facet, even minor ones concerning George's company. Which seemed to prove Fenwick's exact worth, seeing how he had apparently only been back in this country a few weeks after spending considerable time abroad. George sighed while contemplating Sara's unusually disturbed face. What might he not have done had he been able to afford a man like that!

Because of Mark Fenwick the transfer of George's old-established company had gone remarkably smoothly in the end. Not that it hadn't been a wearisome, soul-racking business, trailing on as it had done to start with, and he felt commiseration was due, rather than reproach from Miss Shaw. It could never be an entirely satisfactory way of ending one's working life being taken over by a huge company like Astro Chemicals, even if money-wise he couldn't have done better. He couldn't deny he would have liked to go out with his own flag flying. However, as he had no family to leave it to, apart from a disreputable nephew who rarely looked near, it could be all for the best, once he got used to the idea.

'I'm sorry if you feel you should have been consulted, Sara,' he said with gentle irony, 'but it wasn't altogether my fault. Astro Chemicals insisted on absolute secrecy until everything was finalised and I'm afraid I didn't feel myself in any position to oppose them. And you have been away on holiday these past three weeks, you know. Miss Clegg has been very good, but I surely don't have to tell you I could have done with your assistance on more than one occasion. Having to keep any knowledge of the initial meetings between the two companies from you strained my ingenuity to the utmost, I can tell you, but they refused to have you there. Of course they did supply me with clerical assistance, but it wasn't the same as having you.'

Sara bit her lip, still tense. That last bit, she suspected, had been tacked on to mollify her; George was always kind. Helplessly she shook her head. 'You must put some of it down to hurt pride. It just seems so impossible that I had no notion of what was going on. I knew we were going through a bad spell, naturally, but a good secretary is supposed to know even what her boss is thinking!'

George's mouth twitched humorously. 'It will be something to remember, Sara, that for once I achieved the impossible.' He paused, then continued more wryly, 'I doubt if you'll be able to read anything of what's going on in the head of your new boss. At his best I suspect he's an extremely devious character. You won't lose out, though, my dear,' he hastened to assure her. 'I've arranged that you will stay, and with a substantial rise in salary.'

Sara released a deep breath born of the pain which was moving freely within her now, as she realised what this could mean. 'I'm not sure I want to stay with a new boss, Mr Dent. It all depends.'

'Sara!' George's softening expression hardened with something like alarm, although it was obvious he strove to speak calmly. 'None of us like change. The young imagine they do, the middle-aged, like myself, often think it imperative, but when it actually happens every instinct seems to fight against it. We're really all very adolescent at heart, I suppose, clinging to what we feel is safe, that which is familiar. You're happy with me, Sara, as you know my ways and I've taught you a lot. You know the ins and outs of this company almost as well as I do, and I'm afraid it's directly because of this that Astro Chemicals want you.'

Through stiff lips Sara heard herself protesting, 'But they can't actually know about me personally, George. Someone else might do?'

George gave what might be termed a slightly disapproving smile. 'No to both questions, dear. You'd be impossible to replace immediately. Normally I might have stayed in my present position and there might not have been many noticeable changes. As it is I intend to retire and, as Astro have a lot on just now, they want everything to run as smoothly as possible. Mark Fenwick approached me himself. He spends a lot of time overseas and doesn't want to have to concentrate on this any longer than necessary.'

'Their managing director——' Sara hesitated, her hands damp with perspiration, not yet able to speak his name. 'Wouldn't a firm like Astro Chemicals send someone a little lower down the executive scale?'

Immediately she spoke she knew she had erred. George Dent had his pride and at the moment it was very sensitive. 'Naturally,' he said coolly, 'he won't intend to stay permanently, but this firm is fairly large despite its unfortunate record of the past two years. It's a challenge that appeals to a man like Fenwick, one which he appreciates will be worthwhile. You'll be of great assistance to him. He needs someone like you to act as a kind of buffer, to deal with the masses of inconsequential enquiries he's going to get from personnel, anyway for the first six months.'

'Did he . . .' again Sara had to struggle with her breathing before she could go on, 'did he ask my name?'

'No, although I may have mentioned it. I imagine I

must have done when I was explaining how able you are. I hope you're not going to be difficult over this, Sara?'

'But six months!' Sara sounded despairing even to her own ears. George didn't know, he couldn't guess!

'It's not a lifetime, girl.' George's brows drew together with his first hint of real impatience. 'Mark Fenwick assured me he will look after you well. You must know what this take-over means to me, Sara. Besides, you'll be much better off.'

Rather desperately Sara shook her head, feeling she was being swept by the tide, weakly, towards a man she never wanted to see again. 'I just don't like the idea of working for a stranger, not a man like that anyway.'

'I think you will, Sara.' George was openly persuasive now. 'You've a good brain, it could take you a long way if you make the most of this chance. You don't know this man, do you?' His glance sharpened, as if it had only just occurred to him that something must account for Sara's white, stricken face. He wasn't an over-observant employer, but he couldn't remember seeing her like this before. He didn't flatter himself it was because he was leaving. He was old enough to be her father or more and, indeed, had always looked on her as he might have done the young daughter his wife and he had never had. Not that many employers, he realised dryly, would consider such fetching elegance in such a light. That his young secretary had more than her fair share of charm was something he was quite aware of but, at the same time, he also knew he was a happily married man. He pondered, his mind going idly back. 'You did work for a London firm, didn't you, Sara, before you came here? But you couldn't have been with them more than a few months. If I remember you were very young.'

Sara hated half-truths, but on this occasion she decided it might be wiser to resort to them. She lowered her head so George couldn't see her eyes. 'Actually it was Astro Chemicals I worked for.'

'Good gracious!' George looked startled, even amazed.

'I suppose you must have told me and I'd forgotten?'

'Don't worry,' she smiled mirthlessly, 'I left of my own accord. At least ...'

'Phew! Oh, well, that's a relief.' Visibly he relaxed, not noticing her small hesitation. 'You must have held a very junior position. I don't suppose you ever got near anyone in top management, although I can understand this might be what's worrying you now. Actually it's not something I think you need bother to mention to Mr Fenwick—unless you particularly want to?'

'I—I did occasionally see those at the top,' she faltered, pain again—the old misery she had hoped she had forgotten rising so swiftly she almost cried out. 'As a matter of fact,' she rushed on, as a crazy, half-witted idea struck her, 'I did once have words of a kind with Mark Fenwick. I think he took a sort of instinctive dislike to me. This is why I don't think it would be a good idea for me to stay here and work for him.'

George threw back his grey head and laughed as if with relief. 'Youngsters can be over-sensitive, Sara. It might be nearer the mark, though I'm afraid not so flattering, to say a man like Mark Fenwick probably scarcely noticed your existence. I'd be willing to wager he forgot about you in five minutes. What on earth did you have words about anyway?' he asked curiously. 'I wouldn't have thought a man in Fenwick's position would communicate on the lower levels at all.'

'I'm sure you're right.' It took every scrap of Sara's ingenuity to pretend she hadn't noticed George's last query. She hesitated, then, as George seemed about to put his question again, promised rashly, 'I realise I owe you a lot, George, and as my London days were brief and now very far away I could be getting things out of perspective. If you like I'll try to stay until Mr Fenwick at least gets settled in. I can't guarantee, however, that he'll want me.'

'That seems fair enough.' As Sara had hoped, George was too relieved and preoccupied to probe further. Instead he said kindly, 'Sometimes it pays to face up to old incidents. This way you often find they don't exist any more and you can forget about them. I'm sure Mark Fenwick will prove a challenge to work for, if you can keep your head.'

'Keep my head?' Sara was puzzled by George's dry, teasing tones.

His mouth quirked ironically although his eyes were just a shade anxious. 'You must have noticed, Sara, even if you were still very young, that Mark Fenwick is an extremely attractive man. He still is, and I shouldn't like to think I was throwing you to the wolves. In this case it's only one, of course, but perhaps you should be careful. I'd better warn you—as an old friend, my dear, not your employer—that Mr Fenwick has a bit of a reputation with women, while you, I believe, are particularly innocent. What I'm trying to say, Sara, in my clumsy fashion, is that I wouldn't want to see you hurt.'

Sara forced a laugh which sounded, she hoped, light and airy, the exact opposite of how she was feeling. 'I appreciate your concern, Mr Dent, but don't worry. I do recall a little of Mr Fenwick's reputation. Anyway, he's probably married now and settled down.'

'You could be right,' George nodded with relief and a little embarrassment. 'I suppose we shouldn't be discussing his private affairs which certainly don't affect his business acumen, whatever state they're in. I have no doubt of his ability in this direction. I have also no doubt that you'll find your small difference with him, whatever it was, quite easily forgotten.'

If only it would be like that, Sara thought despairingly as she travelled home that evening. It had been a big enough shock to learn, after her holiday, of George's imminent departure without the additional blow of discovering that they were now a subsidiary of Astro Chemicals. She had known there was something in the wind before she had gone, there had been meetings of the shareholders, etc., but no one firm had been specifically mentioned. Having decided

George was merely at the stage of putting out feelers it was a shock to learn of this! He accused Mark of being devious, but he was surely a little this way himself! On the pretext of tidying up after five, when George had gone, she had searched through various files but hadn't found any specific reference to Astro's anywhere, not until last week, while she had still been away, so it couldn't have been something she had overlooked. Time had passed as she had sat numbly at her desk, her eyes blindly fixed to a piece of paper which told her nothing that George hadn't already divulged. She sat until she realised there was nothing she could do about it, just as, no matter how she wished it, she could never alter the past.

Swiftly she had run a comb through her fluffy brown hair which she usually wore in the office close and smooth about her small, neat head. Her hair was lovely, but her eyes were perhaps her best feature, widely spaced and of a brilliant, quite dazzling blue framed by an extravagance of dark lashes. The mouth she applied a touch of lipstick to was rose red, not really needing any extra adornment. From the past, unheralded came a voice, 'Blue eyes, red mouth, white skin, hair like silk, an irresistible combination.' Well, it hadn't proved so in the end! Hastily Sara clamped down on such futile reminiscence and rising quickly had grabbed her mac, belting it tightly to her small waist before making her way to the lift and thus to her bus stop.

For the last two, almost three years she had lived with her aunt and uncle in their hotel on the outskirts of the city. Sara liked to think it was on the outskirts but it was really fairly central and near enough her place of work to make it convenient to stay there. She tried to believe she enjoyed living in a hotel where there were many more facilities than she could ever afford in digs, but secretly she knew she would sometimes give anything to have just an ordinary home.

Lightly she jumped off the bus on which she had travelled the few miles from work and walked quickly down

the street until she came to where the hotel stood. It was
set well back on a gravelled drive decorated with ornamental
shrubs, the road around it which led to the garages being
tarred. The entire façade spoke of quiet luxury and usually
Sara felt proud each time she stopped to look at it properly.
Tonight, when for some undefinable reason she paused to
stare at it, she was conscious of mixed feelings. Her grandfather had started it, after he had trained under a famous
chef in France and married a French girl, and together
they had begun here in a small way. His elder son, Sara's
uncle René, now carried on and he had expanded the
property until it had over a hundred rooms. Sara didn't
live in the family apartment as it was already crowded with
her aunt and uncle and two cousins. She had a small room
at the top of the hotel for which she insisted on paying a
small sum each week, making up the deficiency by helping
out in the evenings when they were short of staff. It might
not be a very large hotel, but it did have a good star rating
and was extremely popular with tourists and business men
visiting the city. Sara frowned, as she stood there, to recall
how eager she had been three years ago to leave it to try
her luck in London, then how she had almost slunk back to
hide her bruised heart, where no one in that great metro-
polis might see. She wasn't so young now, though, or quite
so naïve as the eighteen-year-old girl she had been then.

As she crossed the gravelled area and entered the foyer
she bumped almost immediately into her aunt and uncle.
She remembered with a start of dismay they were going
out that evening.

'Oh, gosh!' she exclaimed childishly, refuting the advanced years she had laid claim to only minutes ago, 'I
forgot!'

'Naturally you always forget something like this, Sara,'
her aunt sighed with some exasperation while Uncle René
laid a placating hand on his wife's arm. 'Mary has asked to
be away early and I promised you would take over on

reception for an hour or two. Not until seven-thirty, but I do like having everything arranged.'

'Of course.' Perfunctorily she kissed her aunt's cheek as they departed, returning Uncle René's warm smile as he winked. Aunt Loretta was not half as formidable as she occasionally sounded, but she did like everyone to toe the line! They were off to a silver wedding do, she remembered, and it was unlikely they would be back early but Sara didn't mind. Tonight, for the first time in a long time, she wanted to be alone with her thoughts.

Her room was on the top floor and blissfully quiet. Now, as she reached it, she thrust her key into the lock and closed the door firmly behind her. Here at least was privacy, the opportunity she sought to lick wounds she had long considered healed. Might have stayed healed, she thought desperately, if that last interview with George hadn't seemed to rip them open.

Sara was scarcely aware of the half sob that rose to her throat as she tore off her outdoor things on her way to run a bath, letting them drop in an untidy heap at her feet, a thing she didn't normally do. Shivering, she threw a handful of bath salts into the steaming water before tearing off her brief, silky underwear, recalling as if it was yesterday another hand which had undone the lacy bra besides her own. He hadn't been particularly gentle either.

His hand ... With a soft moan she slid beneath the softly scented water, helpless to do anything but let her insistent thoughts carry her back.

'I don't think it's a good idea to go to London,' Uncle René said anxiously. 'You've had a good training. It was decided you should work here, and I don't see why you should change your mind. I know you've just lost both parents, Sara, and this has undoubtedly unsettled you, but wouldn't they be happier to know you were safely here with us?'

Dear Uncle René with his profound belief in the here-after! Momentarily Sara felt tears of affection sting her

eyes. In so many ways he was like Daddy. Aunt Loretta
was good, too. She couldn't have wished for more kindly
relations, only they didn't understand why she felt she
must get away. Every time she looked at Uncle René she
saw her father. When he and Aunt Loretta were together
she remembered her parents, so consistently that after
several weeks the pain hadn't lessened. Sometimes, although
she felt rather ashamed of it, she had a deep longing to be
held close to someone and really comforted, but, again like
her parents, neither her aunt or uncle were very demons-
trative. It would embarrass them greatly, she suspected, if
with her impulsive seeking after warmth she should throw
her arms around them and cling. It would be better for
everyone if she could get away, if only until she pulled herself together. In London, so big, noisy and congested, she
might find forgetfulness if nothing else.

'If you were a plain little thing ...' Loretta sighed, her
eyes studying Sara doubtfully. Then, as if realising that,
like an opening rosebud, Sara was quite unconscious of
her looks, she added, 'I will only allow you to go, child, if
you promise to take sensible clothing. It can be difficult
enough learning to live in a great city without having to
ward off herds of aspiring young men!'

From a highly intelligent woman, who would most certainly have been capable of running a first class hotel single-
handed, this sounded faintly ludicrous, and while Sara
vaguely understood her aunt's fears she felt she couldn't
agree with her. Sara's flights into romance so far, perhaps
due to an over-strict, half French father, had been restrained
chiefly to her imagination. Certainly the mental picture of
being chased by herds of young men merely caused her to
smile wanly, and the idea of a heavy serge skirt acting as a
suitable deterrent almost changed her smile to a giggle!

Swiftly she sobered, her inmost sense of propriety assert-
ing itself. 'I couldn't think of anything so frivolous at such
a time, Aunt Loretta. It is for me a time of mourning. I
simply feel I must go, that's all.'

'Well, perhaps you're right.' Loretta wasn't an over-sensitive woman, but lately Sara's blue eyes seemed to haunt her and she was too busy for this kind of thing. Sara was a funny girl, not so easy to read as her own daughter, nor, Loretta suspected, as easy to manage. At eighteen she was, of course, of an age to do more or less as she chose. Maybe she might be better in London, no matter what René said. 'John Miles——' she referred to a man who had used the hotel regularly for years. 'You're sure he can fix you up with a job?'

'Yes,' Sara's voice changed eagerly. 'He has a cousin who's chief accountant with a large firm. He's promised to take me, if I pass my interview. John sees no reason why I shouldn't.'

'Without experience?' Uncle René didn't sound impressed.

'To get experience,' Sara corrected, smiling. 'I'll only be starting in a very junior position. And don't you see, if I do come back I could be so much more useful to you?'

'You're that already,' Uncle René replied ruefully. 'You've done well at your business college, Sara. I don't think anyone could fault you.'

'Thank you, darling,' Sara smiled gently, her uncle's generous praise making her feel ashamed of her previous doubts about his affection. 'It's just that I would like to see a little more of the world.'

'Spread your wings a little, *mademoiselle*, like a butterfly?' Occasionally, for effect in the hotel or when he was moved, René's French mother was allowed to express herself through him. 'You must be careful, *chérie*, butterflies are easily damaged.'

'But I'm not a butterfly, Uncle René.' Sara's pink mouth curved ruefully as she shook her lustrous head. 'I only wish I were!'

They gave in, in the end, both of them, because the hotel took so much of their attention. It was a good hotel and busy and, when the moment came, Sara was surprised to find herself very sorry to leave it. It was a far cry from Oxford where her father had been a don, but in the short time she had lived there she had found it interesting. Confusing, too, but this she chose to disregard. Uncle René and Aunt Loretta had given her a home and affection when she had most needed it and for this she would always be grateful. Her bags packed she departed for London and the hostel where she must stay until she found a room. This in the end she never managed to do. Not only was rented accommodation hard to find; her stay in London was to prove shorter than she had foreseen.

Astro Chemicals, or Enterprises as it was often called, owing to its other involvements, occupied a huge building. There were so many floors and so many offices on each that Sara gave up trying to count them. 'It's rather like a rabbit warren,' she wrote home to Coventry. 'We all seem to scuttle in and out and I still get lost. Also I feel a very small rabbit!'

She actually was lost when Dicky Gordon found her one day. Standing in the middle of a kind of crossroads in the corridors, she wasn't sure which way to go.

'Need any help?' he enquired lazily, and she swung around startled at the sound of his voice, the thick carpeting having muffled his approach. She saw a tall, fairhaired man, perhaps in his middle twenties, whose goodlooking face sharpened with interest as he met Sara's startling blue eyes. 'Are you lost?'

'Yes,' she replied breathlessly. Then, because he looked so friendly in a place which still struck her a little coldly, she laughed, 'Are you?'

'Not really.' There was a hint of wariness, but she didn't see it.

'Oh—I meant I haven't seen you around.' Which was a crazy thing to say, really, as hundreds of people were employed here and she knew scarcely anybody.

'I'm up on top,' he grinned, 'among the gods, learning to be one.'

'Oh, poor you,' she smiled back, thinking he was the first person she hadn't felt nervous with since she arrived. Not that she really believed he belonged with the top floor executives. He looked too casual, too unweighed down—if there was such an expression—by the world's troubles.

When he posed a suddenly abject stance she giggled, although she was not a girl given to frivolity with strangers, especially when they were attractive young men. She could recall laughing in the wind, at racing clouds and things like horses galloping free in fields with their tails streaming, but never before like this. Yet there was nothing sexy in their lighthearted exchange. They were rather like two children playing truant for a few short minutes from school. Sara didn't see how his eyes lit with interested speculation.

'Tell me your name,' he said.

'Is this an order?' she smiled. 'A command from the gods?'

He composed his face so threateningly she giggled again. 'You can consider it as such.'

'Then,' she sobered meekly, 'it seems I must obey. Sara Shaw. And yours?'

'Lesser subjects,' he growled, 'aren't supposed to ask.'

'Please,' she coaxed, because he seemed so much like a small boy.

'Could I deny you anything, I wonder?' He seemed immediately riveted by her anxious expression. 'Richard Gordon, Dicky to my friends.'

'How do you do,' she murmured, trying belatedly to be formal although his immediate effect on her was as the brother she had never had. It came to her suddenly, with a slight shock, that he might be interested in her, other than a sister! He was actually giving Sara Shaw, in her prim white blouse and trim navy skirt, a second look!

'I say,' he whispered, with a rather mysteriously quick glance across his shoulder, 'are you doing anything this evening?'

It was too much like a romantic short story to be true.

Furtively Sara pinched herself to make sure she wasn't
imagining it all. She wasn't sure she wanted to go out with
Dicky Gordon, if this was what he was getting around to.
It had boosted her ego slightly, given her a faint feeling of
sophistication to have been able to talk with him so casually, but she felt a bit wary of going further. Not that he
appeared anything but respectable in his well tailored suit;
he had a nice friendly face, too. Still she hesitated.

'I asked you a question, young Sara.' He smiled yet gave
another anxious look around him.

'I'm sorry,' she answered hastily, 'I mean—no. I'm not
doing anything in particular.'

'Sara,' he spoke rapidly now, 'would you come out with
me? Nothing special, so you needn't bother to dress up. We
can get to know each other better.'

This sounded reasonable—and very nice. And he did
work here, which must count for something, at least it
helped to allay her fears. All the stories she'd heard about
what happened to indiscriminate young girls in big bad
cities faded into the background. 'Yes,' she agreed, putting
down his quickening impatience to an urge to get back to
work. Which reminded her she was in no position to be
loitering here herself.

'Fine,' he nodded. 'I'll pick you up at the end of your
street. Wherever that may be?'

She told him and added a word of thanks. She wasn't
sure if gratitude at this stage was in order, but it seemed to
please him.

'See you later then, chick. But one thing ...' He paused
and she prompted, 'Yes?'

'Keep this under your hat, won't you, Sara? I can't stand
the usual office chat. It can be very far from the mark, you
know, and I don't want you involved in it.'

Sara gazed after him, rather dazed by the encounter and
not sure in her heart if she had done the right thing. Had
she been too impulsive, accepting an invitation from a com-
parative stranger, even one who worked in the same firm as

herself? Was it sensible to allow the temptation to make a friend to persuade her to overlook all the unwritten rules she had been brought up with? Richard Gordon seemed pleasant enough and she had a sudden desire for someone to laugh with. There couldn't surely be anything so wrong about that?

Later she wondered if he would really turn up. Casual dates were often just as casually dropped and he might easily change his mind. She didn't let her hopes build too high and was somewhat surprised to find him waiting as he had promised at the end of her road.

'I'm glad you came,' he said.

'So am I,' she replied as she slid into the opulent little sports car beside him. She was a fraction startled by such luxury. Whatever else, he must have a better job than she had to be able to afford such obvious class!

He took her somewhere quiet. She had been rather apprehensive about this as instinctively, after she had had time to think about it, she had sensed he could be very outgoing, certainly not reticent. About this she must have been mistaken as he proved more sombre than lively, so much so that she was forced to decide he was extremely moody.

They saw a film and she might have suspected he had seen it previously as he talked all the way through it. In comparison to his former silence she found it a bit unnerving. Later, because he still reminded her of a small boy, she forgave him. It wasn't difficult as she had been aware of his eyes on her almost throughout the film and some feminine part of her felt flattered. Dangerous flattery, she warned herself, when at the end he grabbed her hand and told her she was sweet.

On the whole, in spite of his despondency, he appeared much taken by her. Sara cautiously didn't intend being rushed or to let a few teasing compliments go to her head. She liked him just as much as she had done that afternoon, but not even when he took her by surprise and swiftly kissed her goodnight did she feel thrilled by him. His thanks for a wonderful evening didn't impress either, but she simply smiled and managed a dignified goodnight.

During the following weeks she went out with him again from time to time, but she didn't seem to get to know him any better. Yet if theirs was a relationship doomed not to develop into anything special, for some reason or other, Sara only felt relieved. While she pondered over him occasionally he wasn't, in fact, the only man she met.

Like most young people in her lowly position she was much put on to fetch and carry. She ran the odd errands that kept her late for lunch, which sometimes she considered herself fortunate to manage at all! Wednesday proved no exception. A few minutes before one there was an urgent message from Management.

'A job for you, Sara,' Aline Gregg, the head of the department's secretary cried. 'Some information required from Accounts. You're to take it straight up.'

'At once?'

'When Mr Trevor gets it together.'

'But my lunch?' Sara dared to protest faintly.

'Work is a privilege at your age, dear. Don't abuse it with thoughts of food!' Miss Gregg swept out, obviously having no intention of forgoing her own lunch. She departed and seemed to take the rest of the department with her.

Sara strove to hold on to her equilibrium, waiting as patiently as she was able. This time she didn't really mind being general dogsbody. On the top floor she might just happen to catch sight of Richard. She must remember, he was always telling her Dicky for short! He was most mysterious about his exact section and she was filled with a curiosity she might not have possessed if he hadn't been so secretive. At heart, she was sure he wasn't so dissembling, but he did rather tend to put her off whenever she pressed him for closer details. She was sure his evasiveness must be due to some past embarrassment but couldn't help feeling slightly hurt that he didn't apparently trust her.

At last Mr Trevor gathered the required information,

passing it on to Sara with a faint smile on his elderly face
and instructions to take it straight up.

'Of course, Mr Trevor,' she said, nervously taking hold
of the large folder.

'Mr Fenwick's office, mind you. Nowhere else.'

Did everyone think it naturally followed that a girl of
her age must be a fool? Moodily Sara shook her head as she
took the lift to the top floor. Mr Trevor was quite as nice as
John Miles said he would be, but she doubted if either he or
Miss Gregg ever saw her as a real person. They didn't seem
to understand that to leave one's family, to work so far from
home, required one to be extremely adult.

All the same she didn't feel too confident as she left the
lift and found the way to her hallowed destination. Here
it was deathly quiet and there was certainly no sign of
Dicky. Like everywhere else in the huge building there
seemed an extravagance of shining glass and wide, polished
surfaces. A perfection of modern, clinically clean space, only
up here the carpeting seemed so much thicker than down
below; her feet almost sank.

Tentatively she knocked on the outer door marked
Managing Director. On receiving no reply she opened it
carefully and went in. She knew Mr Fenwick's secretary
was called Miss Drew, but as there was no sign of her it was
sensible to suppose she was out at lunch. So what did she
do now? About to lay the folder on Miss Drew's desk, she
heard a slight stir from the inner office that warned her
someone was there. Probably Mr Fenwick himself. Sara
frowned. Should she leave the package on Miss Drew's desk
in the hope he would discover it, or should she take it in?

As she floundered with what appeared an insurmountable
problem the door at which she had been staring opened
suddenly and a man stood there. To Sara's startled eyes he
looked both annoyed and impatient.

'Ah, at last!' His eyes fell on the folder clutched tightly
in Sara's hot hands. 'Why didn't you bring that straight in,
girl, instead of dithering around out here?'

Sara's hands were not only hot, they trembled as she made to pass the folder to him and she was confused again as he turned abruptly and went back into his office. Did he expect her to follow? Feeling more naïve than ever, she did, not knowing what else to do. He was arrogant, he sounded overbearing. Very few girls of her age, Sara decided, would know exactly what to do when confronted with a man like this. She could only remember his eyes, they seemed to see right through her. No man ought to have eyes like that. Drawing no comfort from such a thought, she went after him, very cautiously although she did not realise it.

Carefully, aware suddenly that he had resumed his seat behind his desk and was watching her, Sara walked self-consciously towards him and laid the folder before him. 'I'm sorry, Mr Fenwick,' she faltered, taking an immediate step backwards, 'Mr Trevor asked me to see this reached the right hands and when Miss Drew wasn't in I wasn't sure what to do with it.'

'Really, Miss—whoever you are,' his sculptured mouth curled, 'is such a trite little apology supposed to impress me?'

His eyes derided her and she felt herself quiver as she stared into their smouldering depth. Swiftly she blinked, sensing he was in a bad mood which might have nothing personally to do with her own behaviour, yet this didn't prevent her from retorting unwisely. Miss Drew might have warned her it would have been better to have stayed silent, but Miss Drew wasn't there, and neither, unfortunately, was anyone else. Sara, allowing an anxious indignation to have its way, said hotly, 'It wasn't supposed to be an apology, Mr Fenwick, simply an explanation. You see, I've never been up here before so I didn't know you would be in here—but you can't blame me for that!'

CHAPTER TWO

MARK FENWICK expelled a deep breath, his eyes narrowing sharply as he regarded the pale, slightly defiant girl before him. 'Have you been anywhere before, I wonder?' His voice seemed full of a dry mockery. 'Sometimes I'd give anything to know where they find them!'

Doubtfully Sara stared at him, his almost open insult bringing a fine colour to her skin. His desk was piled high with papers, an untouched luncheon tray residing among them. She wondered why Miss Drew hadn't pointed out that going without meals could have a disastrous effect on a man's temper. His eyes chilled her and she thought they might supply the answer. No one would dare advise a man with eyes like that. They were a peculiar light grey, seemingly related to ice. 'Mr Fenwick,' she said dazedly, 'I think your remark is unfair.'

'Oh, you do, do you?' He leant forward fractionally so she could see the hard, clean line of his jaw. 'Has no one told you that office juniors, and I doubt you are no more, are not in any position to question any remark I choose to make?'

This, of course, if she had any sense, was her cue to bow out, after making suitable expressions of penitence. But something seemed to hold her there, a captive of his icy stare, as if drawn magnetically to that which frightened her. 'I'm afraid I find it difficult to accept something I don't agree with,' she answered rather inanely.

'So,' his handsome if ruthless face darkened as he surveyed her, 'we are not only audacious but impudent as well! Yet I could have sworn you were a well brought up young lady. Tell me, Miss ...' he paused so obviously she felt forced to supply her name, 'tell me, Miss Shaw,' he continued sarcastically, when she meekly obliged, 'are you

23

really as naïve as you sound or have you a calculating brain bent on drawing my attention?'

Startled, Sara's blue eyes widened and she was conscious of a peculiar feeling of near shock moving through her. Her heart beat rapidly so that she felt the need to place a protective hand over it and her blue eyes went strangely dark. She was aware of an odd tension between herself and this man who watched her so coolly, which seemed to have little to do with her lowly position or the apparent irreverence of her answers. Perhaps the trauma within her, the electric tightness in her breast was simply because she sensed his intense irritation with life in general. Already she had learnt enough to realise when anything niggled the heads of the departments they tended to take it out on their staff. Yet while every instinct warned that Mark Fenwick hadn't had a good morning she couldn't help feeling indignant that he should choose to get rid of his resentment on her!

Her own resentment tilted her rounded chin defensively. 'Why should I try to attract your attention, Mr Fenwick?' Very foolishly she made it sound as if it was the last thing on earth she would wish to do.

Surveying her closely, his mouth tightened and he appeared to cast aside any notion he might be unfair. It became abundantly clear that he had decided slender little nobodies, with a too innocent look about them, made ideal scapegoats, and his morning had been so harassing he felt vaguely in need of one.

'Why should you try to attract my attention?' he reiterated, sneering, his eyes glittering on her flushed young face. 'How am I supposed to know the answer to that? I do know, though, that some of you seem almost willing to faint at my feet when the mood takes you. Only the other day a girl ran after me with a handkerchief which was never mine. If I feel like challenging such optimism occasionally, why shouldn't I?'

Sara blinked, the colour in her cheeks deepening with

what she knew must seem like guilt. It had been Gwen, one of the other girls in Accounts, who had run after him with that handkerchief and Sara had been with her at the time. Gwen hadn't said who he was and Sara hadn't asked, but she realised she might have recognised him, remembered him because of his tallness, the breadth of his shoulders, the strength of his profile as he had turned to glance swiftly at Gwen and shake his head. Sara hadn't been aware he had seen her, but she realised instinctively now that he had done, if only out of the corner of his eye. The knowledge rankled as if he had openly accused her of some sort of conspiracy of which she was entirely innocent, yet what could she say? How could she defend either herself, or the unfortunate Gwen, without incurring his further wrath? Up here in his well appointed office, which would have put many an elegant drawing room to shame, he seemed entirely unapproachable, from her position, anyway! For Gwen's sake, however, it seemed imperative that she issued even a small note of protest. Clasping her trembling hands together, she said quickly, 'I'm sure Gw—the girl wouldn't realise who you were, Mr Fenwick. People do tend to look alike in a crowd.'

There was a moment's sharp silence while Sara continued to quiver almost visibly. How had she ever dared to insinuate that he could pass for one of the common herd? Wasn't she tempting fate to so much as suggest such a thing when not even his worst enemy could deny he must stand out anywhere! The Mark Fenwicks of this world were noticed wherever they went. Her eyes lifted again with a kind of nervous awe to his face. He looked arrogant and aloof, as she supposed befitted his position, and even the slight ruffling of his thick, dark hair as he ran an impatient hand over it only seemed to add to his distinction.

Suddenly, to her surprise, when dramatically she felt her last moment might well have come, he smiled. It might only be a dry twist of his lips, but she felt instantly relieved by even this much. 'I think the conversation is getting rather out of hand, Miss Shaw. I'm sure you'll agree? Perhaps if you were to offer me a handkerchief I would react differently.'

'I would never dare—now,' Sara was somewhat startled to hear herself reply. More so to find herself smiling faintly back at him. It seemed impossible not to. Until this moment she hadn't realised that along with his other notable attributes he might also have quite a dangerous charm. She could feel it now quite distinctly and with a quick shudder she stiffened against it, as if it posed some direct threat.

This time, as if he sensed her uncertainty, his eyebrows quirked upwards and she retreated another step, fully expecting a formal dismissal. Her surprise must have been reflected in her face as she heard him ask her to pour his coffee. 'If it's cold you can ring for some more,' he advised curtly, his face grim again.

'It's not.' Apprehensively she did a sort of quick dive for the coffee pot and found it hot. The dark brown liquid spilt a little over the side of the cup and she silently cursed her unusual clumsiness. 'I'm sorry,' she apologised, not knowing whether to offer him sugar and milk as they were just as easily within his reach as hers. The aromatic smell of the coffee tantalised her nostrils almost as much as Mark Fenwick did her senses. Anxiously she placed his coffee on the desk beside him and grasped the milk jug.

This he ignored with a mere shake of his head, something he was good at, she recalled fretfully. He helped himself, though, to two spoonfuls of sugar, so she learnt he liked his coffee black and sweet. Not that she was likely to need such knowledge again. Pouring the M. D.'s coffee must be a unique experience for a lowly typist, one not likely to be repeated.

'Would you care for a cup? Isn't this your lunch hour?'

At the sound of his voice, Sara almost jumped. She had been so busy noting things down she had quite forgotten her lunch. There wouldn't be time to go now, not unless she was prepared to court trouble from Aline Gregg. It didn't really matter, she tried to convince herself, but couldn't prevent her eyes going hungrily to the pile of succulent-looking ham sandwiches.

'Help yourself,' he drawled sardonically, as if some experiences were actually unique to him too. He gestured towards the food with a careless hand as he rose to open a cupboard door, drawing forth a roll of plastic cups. 'I don't know how these ever got in here, but it's probably high time they were used. Here,' he selected one after removing the cellophane wrapping, 'fill it up for yourself while I check if Trevor has sent everything I asked for.'

While he returned to his desk and opened the folder to pursue the contents, Sara stared down at the cup in her hand. The sandwiches were beautiful, better than any she had tasted since coming here, if only her leaping nerves would allow her to enjoy them. What would people think if they could see her now? Mark Fenwick mustn't realise what he was doing! A wave of surprising desolation seemed to strike her. When he stopped to think about it—if he ever did—he would most likely put her down as another silly girl who had tried to take liberties with him. Of course she hadn't asked to eat his sandwiches, nor, she thought, unaware of her expressive eyes, had her manner suggested she would like to. One was enough; she certainly wouldn't accept more, even should he beg her.

'Go on, Miss Shaw, eat them up.' Mark Fenwick, almost as if he read her thoughts, glanced at her impatiently over a sheaf of papers. 'I remember at your age I was always hungry. How old are you, by the way?'

'Eighteen.' Throwing caution to the winds, she took another sandwich while, to her astonishment, he refilled her cup himself.

'Eighteen?' His gaze was suddenly keen as he laid the papers to one side, studying her contemplatively. 'I can nearly double that, but I can't say I'd like to put the clock back. I shouldn't like to face all the pitfalls of youth's inexperience again.'

She didn't doubt he had coped better than most; the sensuous, yet cynical curve of his hard mouth convinced her! Reprehensibly she choked on a single crumb which served to remind her sharply of the possible ignominy of her position. Hastily she put down her cup, jumping up from the chair on which she had been sitting. She was only a yard away from the door when his voice caught her.

'Miss Shaw, where are you going?'

Her thin shoulders stiffening against his dictatorial tones, she stopped abruptly but didn't turn around. 'If Miss Drew should come back and find me here I would have to account for—for . . .'

He showed immediate impatience with her faltering hesitation. 'You mean you would have to account for sharing my lunch? Come and sit down, Miss Shaw. I didn't think you could be so incredibly stupid! Not even Miss Drew would be foolish enough to imagine I'd allow you to wander in here and help yourself.'

For Miss Drew to be told he had asked her might cause even worse speculation. 'I'm sorry, Mr Fenwick,' she said unhappily, 'but I really should be going.' With attempted humour she smiled slightly. 'You wouldn't want me to be late for work.'

'I said sit down!'

This time it was so much an order that she had no other recourse than to obey. He appeared to have lost interest in his papers, but Sara didn't flatter herself she had his attention because he was really interested in herself. It probably diverted him to torment her a little.

He got to his feet and going over to a cabinet poured himself a drink. 'Tell me, Miss Shaw,' he wandered back, standing beside his desk, staring broodingly down at her, 'whereabouts in London do you live? I suspect you're one of the rare breed who still like to live at home. You don't look worldly enough to be let loose on your own.'

Sara glanced at him swiftly, a little shaken that he should be asking her anything so personal. It wasn't as if he sounded really curious. 'I do live away from home. In a hostel.'

'So I was wrong. You do have a streak of independence.'

'In my case it's nothing to boast about, Mr Fenwick. I come from Coventry and would find it difficult to commute from there each day.'

He seemed to consider her for a long moment and she sat uneasily beneath his narrow gaze, wishing he wouldn't tower over her so. He made her feel very insignificant and again came the suspicion he was merely using her as a kind of diversion. Something which fate had blown along to amuse him for a few minutes. She had no doubt, from the rumours she had heard, that he was well used to manipulating women. His affairs were legend, but he always ended them before things grew too complicated. This was according to office gossip and, although Dicky had warned her about it, there was invariably some truth in it somewhere. Sara's pulse missed a beat again and her limbs felt curiously weak as she allowed herself to wonder what it must be like to be involved with a man like Mark Fenwick. Dicky Gordon by comparison seemed a mere boy, though why she should compare the two at all she had no idea.

From uneasy meditation on romantic seduction she forced her mind back to more mundane matters—how to escape from this office and get back to her own; how to do so quickly and with dignity. She became aware that Mark Fenwick was speaking again.

'How come you left your home town for London? Hostel life can't be all that inviting.'

'I felt like a change,' she answered steadily.

'And your parents?'

'Parents?' She tried to prevent her cheeks going white.

'Yes,' she heard a soft note of censure. 'Were they quite willing you should come here?'

'I didn't have to ask them.'

'Why not? Did you not at least consult them?',

'Mr Fenwick,' she flared, at the derision in his eyes, 'do

you have to probe to the bitter end? If you must know, I don't have them any more. There was an accident.'

'I see. I'm sorry,' he added formally, his expression watchful rather than kinder as he considered her pale face.

Sara was glad he didn't go on about it. He couldn't really say very much as they were still more or less strangers and empty condolences never appealed to her. Mark Fenwick wouldn't be much good at handing out sympathy. He might hand out plenty, but not that.

'A hostel can't be the most satisfactory place to live,' he mused, his eyes still on her. 'What do you find to do with yourself of an evening? You can't lead a very licentious life, bound by all sorts of rules and regulations.'

'Of course not——' She stopped suddenly, fingers of pink stealing across the whiteness of her skin, emphasising its translucent quality.

He saw the flush and his eyes narrowed in frank appreciation—and speculation. 'But you have friends. Boy-friends?'

Sara didn't feel she must confess about Dicky Gordon. They certainly didn't have any licentious relationship, whatever the great Mark Fenwick chose to think! Hedging, she replied, 'I've been out with one man, but I only consider him a casual acquaintance.'

He retorted cynically, 'That's the general idea nowadays, isn't it? Keep it light. Women think they can handle even their more passionate moments that way and tend to scream blue murder when occasionally things move beyond their control. Nor do they always believe their indiscretions must usually be paid for, one way or another.'

His sensuous mouth curled as he stared down at his drink, as if in moody contemplation that had nothing directly to do with Sara, but when he spoke it was so sharply she almost jumped. 'Who is this mysterious friend? Have you known him long?'

'No.' Still slightly dazed by his former, clipped outburst, she blinked, 'I've only just met him. That is . . .'

'Yes?' Mark prompted quickly, as she hesitated. 'Pray continue.'

But she was saved by a faint noise in the outer office which obviously heralded another arrival. 'Miss Drew!' Sara breathed, her relief not difficult to detect.

'There you are,' Mark Fenwick taunted. 'Prayers are answered sometimes, it seems. You can escape, now that Miss Drew is about to ring through and remind me that I have a board meeting in ten minutes' time. Go on, young Sara, before I change my mind.'

'Thank you, Mr Fenwick, for my lunch,' Sara stammered, not at all sure what he meant but in no way keen to stop and ask. She was only too thankful he didn't try to detain her longer. In her haste she jumped to her feet. almost stumbling, while he viewed her attempts at a dignified departure with an expression of undisguised impatience. There might have been some amusement there, too. A swift glance at his face, as she fled, seemed to confirm it as a mixture of several things, none of which seemed very flattering.

If Miss Drew was slightly astonished to see a flurry of long, coltish legs rush past her from Mr Fenwick's domain, she was too well trained to show her feelings. Sara scarcely noticed her, in fact she was halfway down her third flight of stairs before she realised she should have taken the lift. Swiftly she changed course, rushing into the lift when it stopped, as if pursued by the devil himself, thankful there was no one around to witness her silly blundering.

She hoped no one would see she was late, but Miss Gregg did, and Sara was forced to confess that Mr Fenwick had ordered her to wait while he went through the papers she had taken up. She didn't say anything about having shared his sandwiches, she doubted if they would have believed her, in any case. She still found it incredible herself. It was one of those things which could only happen once in a lifetime and not something to be bandied around the office. Mark Fenwick would be furious, and with some justification if she did say anything and he heard. He had been kind, she would be the first to admit it. Suddenly Sara shivered as she wondered what else he could be if he chose.

'Didn't his lordship pass any comments?' Gwen wanted to know, possibly because Sara still looked rather distracted.

'None,' Sara couldn't honestly think of any that could be easily passed on. 'I don't suppose,' she added feebly, 'he even noticed I was there.'

Gwen nodded agreement. 'We aren't important enough. They do say, however, he knows all that goes on.'

Miss Gregg flashed her a glacial glance, well aware that her romantic attachment for a married man in the section was not the great secret she wished it was. 'Just get on with your work, girls,' she reprimanded.

Sara sighed. Miss Gregg obviously included her, which she thought slightly unfair as she was only vaguely aware of what the other two were talking about. Miss Gregg was young and smart and Sara couldn't think why she needed to go around with a man who had a wife in the background. Nor could she really believe Mark Fenwick interested himself in such matters, although, like most men, he mightn't be above listening to the grapevine. Deliberately turning off the mental picture she retained of his dark attractiveness, Sara returned ruefully to her typewriter.

For the remainder of the afternoon she worked hard, and it wasn't until it was almost time to go home that she realised nearly all her efforts were directed towards forgetting the man on the top floor. Surely she wasn't going to get as besotted with him as half the female staff appeared to be? With a swift shudder she thrust the possibility aside. It was simply the novelty of the situation that had caught her imagination.

Because she was determined to stop thinking of Mark Fenwick she volunteered to do an hour's overtime in order to tire herself out. It wasn't until she was actually putting on her coat that she discovered she had lost her handbag. She didn't panic, not immediately, not until a quick search through her desk revealed it wasn't there. About to start turning everything upside down again, she paused, aghast. She had had it with her when she had taken those notes to Mark Fenwick. She had dropped it on the floor by her chair when he had asked her to pour his coffee. Then Miss Drew had come in and she had rushed out. It must still be up there. Taking a deep breath, Sara sat down, clasping her arms around herself in order to stop herself trembling. Oh, heavens! What did she do—what could she do now? Maybe they hadn't noticed it as it was dark, like the carpet. Miss Drew might not even have been in Mr Fenwick's office as he had been going out. If she had she would have been much too busy to have seen a small bag under a chair.

The building was almost deserted at this hour. This section was; there was no one whom she could ask for advice. Sara huddled in absolute dismay, biting her lower lip until it almost bled, then began adding up. Three minutes up, three down, two to recover her handbag. If she was lucky, say ten in all—it didn't amount to much. Unhappily she chewed some more. As a mathematical problem it seemed simple enough, but she suspected there might be more to it than that. If the cleaning staff were on, for instance, they might not allow her in. It might be more than they dared risk. No, Sara decided, she only had one chance. Her only hope lay in finding Miss Drew still there. Like herself she could be working late, so if she hurried she might still catch her.

Unfortunately when Sara reached the top floor Miss Drew had gone. The office door was open, much to her surprise, but everyone had gone. Swiftly, feeling as if she were committing some dreadful crime, she went in and looked around, but could see no sign of her shoulder-bag.

It must, it just had to be somewhere! Cautiously, her hands growing sticky with perspiration, she eyed Mr Fenwick's door. Could it still be there? Silently, almost as she had done earlier in the day, she stared at it, trying to persuade herself to go in. He wasn't there—it was only the thought of him that intimidated. At last, irritated by her own cowardly hesitation, she gathered enough courage to push open the door. Once through it she almost gasped aloud to find him sitting at his desk looking straight at her.

She actually jumped, like a small, startled cat and just as vulnerable. Grey eyes speared blue as they stared at each other, Sara's wide with apprehension, his narrowed, holding hers as if on the edge of a sword. It must have been shock, she told herself afterwards, that held her so immobile but it seemed for a moment of time they were locked in combat, that a kind of invisible force sweeping between them rendered her unable to move.

Making a great effort, which hurt so much it might have been physical, she wrenched her gaze from his, her small face scarlet from the unfamiliar and frightening heat of her body. She had truly expected he would be gone. What a fool she had been not to ring first. Why hadn't she thought of it? It would have been so much simpler. Then she wouldn't have felt shaken beyond her depth by some intangible force which she suspected she hadn't the experience to cope with.

'Miss Shaw?'

Half in flight she turned, a slim, completely confused figure, her brown hair whirling in a fine cloud about her face. 'I'm sorry, Mr Fenwick,' she blurted out, 'I didn't know you were here.'

'Obviously not.' His eyes were now sardonic as they caught her bewildered ones. 'This seems to be becoming a habit.'

'Oh, but it's not!' Hastily she tried to control her wobbling voice, her hot cheeks. 'I—that is, I think I left my handbag up here, when I was here earlier, and I'm afraid I can't get home without it. It contains all my money, you see.'

'All of it, Miss Shaw?'

Sara hated his sarcasm but had no recourse other than to go on. It required great effort, though, standing there wholly at the mercy of his dry, glittering gaze. 'Yes, Mr Fenwick. That is until I get paid on Friday. I never have very much at this time of the month, just enough to buy lunch and sometimes dinner.'

'Good lord!'

Because she wasn't sure whether that expressed sorrow or disgust, Sara said nothing, just stood there staring at him helplessly.

His hard mouth compressed and she recognised the familiar impatience. 'Doesn't your hostel supply you with food?'

'Some of it, but you see, when I work late——' she hesitated, not wishing him to think she was complaining, 'I manage very well, Mr Fenwick. I really do.'

He continued to gaze at her coolly and again she was disconcerted to feel peculiar tremors running right through her, and she wished he would look elsewhere. As a child she had been taught that it was rude to stare, but he seemed to have no compunction about it, not regarding her, anyway. She felt he was studying every bit of her and she was in no way composed as his eyes lingered on certain, more obvious places. Yet his eyes were so hard and cold they suggested absolutely nothing she could actually object to.

'Are you sure,' he asked curtly, at last, 'you've really lost your bag, or is it just your money?'

'Why ...' uncertainly she blinked, 'how could I lose one without the other?'

His mouth thinned, as if he restrained himself from saying more, then suddenly she realised what he was getting at. Sparks of anger lit her eyes to a brilliant blue and she felt choked, 'You think I came up here deliberately!'

'It wouldn't be the first time.'

'Oh!' As she turned, horrified, on her heel he was on his feet, his hand coming out to catch her.

'Don't be too hasty, Miss Shaw. I'll admit I might have been, but occasionally in the past I've had good reason to jump to certain conclusions.'

Sara tried to think of a suitable reply but couldn't. Inside she was too frozen to allow the immediate release of even her bursting indignation. As if sensing this he smiled slightly, his eyes resting wryly on her stunned face,

'Before we say anything further, Sara, I suggest we begin looking for this missing bag.'

Numbly Sara nodded, her anger fading as common sense took over. He could just as easily have ordered her out. His hand still held her arm as if he had forgotten about it and his bulk concealed a clear view of the chair she had sat on at lunch time. Swiftly she glanced at him beneath her lashes. 'I was sitting there,' she began.

'I remember,' he cut in, turning to study the chair while Sara jerked her arm free and, taking advantage of his distraction, almost dived under it.

Dismay made her face comical as her eyes flew to his again. 'It's not there!'

Mark Fenwick, she was to discover, had certain qualities which made him what he was. 'If it's not there,' he said quietly, 'Miss Drew must have put it somewhere else.'

Such sensible thinking, Sara found, had a calming effect. Some of the rigidness went immediately out of her, though she still felt tense. 'I expect that is what's happened,' she agreed, following his footsteps eagerly to the outer office.

Unfortunately Miss Drew's desk was locked, the keys missing, and a thorough search of the few open cupboards revealed nothing. Certainly there was no handbag. Sara scarcely realised she was so close behind Mark Fenwick as he examined every nook and cranny, peering anxiously over his shoulder as he opened each door, until he turned and caught her.

'Can't you trust me to look properly, Sara?' his voice was loaded with irritation as he nearly knocked her over. His hand went out, steadying her, his fingers this time far from kind.

Near to him like this she felt herself tremble. When she

raised her eyes and met his she was sure she was drowning in grey, chilly seas. 'My mother used to say no man could,' she retorted rashly.

His eyebrows rose. 'These age-old theories bore me, Miss Shaw. They might die a natural death if women were not so fond of trotting them out.'

'I'm sorry,' she apologised miserably.

'I wonder?' he jeered dryly. 'Tell me, Miss Shaw, do you always give your foolish instincts full rein?'

'It was—it's important that I find my bag.'

He sighed. 'I wasn't referring to your silly little bag, Miss Shaw. I was merely curious as to how far you usually allow your impulsiveness to carry you. Your handbag is missing and you rush up here, with no regard for anyone's convenience!'

'Oh, but,' wide-eyed, Sara faltered, her gaze fixed apprehensively on his grim mouth, 'you can't understand what it means to lose all one's money, Mr Fenwick.'

'Perhaps not,' he frowned, after a moment's silence, during which he closely scrutinised Sara's anxious face. 'I don't suppose I do, but it might teach you not to put all your eggs in one basket in future.'

'Yes,' she murmured meekly, then immediately wondered if she should have said no? Mark Fenwick both puzzled and confused her. Hastily she pulled away from him as she made to go. 'I'm sorry to have been such a nuisance,' she added, mustering every scrap of dignity. 'I promise it won't happen again.'

'Wait a minute!' He was at the door before her, blocking her way, somehow seeming mildly surprised by his own action. 'If you haven't any money, it appears to leave me with no other option but to take you home. I'd better get you something to eat as well. If I'm to play the Good Samaritan I may as well make a good job of it.'

'No!' Sara stood rooted to the spot, quite staggered. His exact phrasing eluded her, but she hated his condescension. With an effort she managed to restrain herself from a sharper refusal. He probably hadn't meant to sound so disparaging. 'No,' she said again, her face growing paler, 'I couldn't let you. I told you before, I can manage.'

'Sara!' Suddenly his mild suggestion was an order. 'Spare me the ordeal of being forced to listen while you dither. I might tell you I'm not acting entirely from benevolence. It so happens I'm feeling rather cynical about women in general this evening and can always relieve my feelings on you.'

How cool he sounded, how censorious when his voice came crisp and hard. Could a woman really be responsible for such derisiveness, or had he just had a bad day? 'I still don't think——' she began, then gasped to find herself literally swept through the door. 'Please,' she entreated feverishly, as his arm propelled her with humiliating speed towards the lift, the grip of his fingers so tight that she decided indignantly he was already beginning to relieve some of the feelings he talked about!

'Stop wriggling,' he muttered indifferently. 'You can stop spluttering and protesting too. Consider this a joint effort. You might have to be prepared to sing for your supper, so you won't owe me a thing.' An observation which if it made sense to him, did not to Sara.

She was relieved, however, that everyone appeared to have gone as they made their way from the building. Even the night porter seemed momentarily to have deserted his post. Not that Mark Fenwick appeared to care who saw them as he stalked silently by her side. What was he thinking about? she wondered despairingly, as she almost ran to keep up with his long strides. Were his dark, shuttered thoughts concentrated on her own follies, or those of this other woman who had apparently let him down in some way?

His car was parked in the space reserved for the hierarchy and, as she stared at it curiously, he inserted his keys and told her to get in. She did so, reluctantly, and he closed the door smoothly, his movements unhurried, as if taking a young typist out for a meal was nothing unusual. With some men it might not be, but Sara was conversant enough with office gossip to know he never took out one of the ordinary staff. Tonight, if he appeared to be breaking one of his own unwritten rules it could only be because of extenuating circumstances.

As it was, Sara felt so completely bewildered by such a sequence of events she could only sit quietly, unable to find breath for further protest. As she stole a swift glance at his grim profile she wondered what he had meant when he had said he wasn't feeling particularly charitable. Surely it was an act of kindness to take pity on a girl who had lost her handbag? He seemed to hint that some woman had let him down, yet what woman could ignore a man like this? Rumours of his romantic entanglements went around, but of course speculation must always be rife about any unmarried, unattached man in his position.

The streets were dark, but she seemed to recognise they were making for the West End. Anxiously she stared out at the bright lights as they passed. She grew even more apprehensive on realising they were in Pall Mall and from St James's Square turned up King Street. From there she wasn't sure where they went next, but she thought it was Bury Street. Alarmed, she was about to protest that she wasn't dressed for anything very smart when she realised, with some constraint, that she would merely be quoting the obvious. She wouldn't give him an excuse for another dry remark. If he considered her navy skirt good enough for anything then she wouldn't argue.

As she feared, the restaurant he took her to wasn't cheap or ordinary in any way and she suspected he had acted deliberately. It was a kind of cellar, a huge one, the decor both vivid and restrained, with an overall air of luxury. Gay painted murals covered the walls and the seating was plushy black velvet against black-topped, steel tables. In the background somewhere was an occasional drum beat of soft music, but nothing obtruded. The whole atmosphere was of elegant sophistication, but contrary to what she had expected, Sara didn't find it at all frightening.

Wryly she noticed how easily Mark Fenwick managed to procure the best attention. It must be nice, she thought, to be the kind of man who had head waiters bowing and smiling, who with a snap of long, lean fingers managed to get instant service while others waited.

He saw her settled before dropping into the seat opposite and he couldn't have been more attentive if she had been dressed like a queen. 'I hope it pleases you, Miss Shaw?'

If he hoped still to disconcert her she wouldn't give him the satisfaction! Unfortunately her tongue tripped, giving the mistaken impression she was dazed. 'Oh, yes. That is . . .'

His eyes glinted with a slight satisfaction she wasn't really surprised to see. 'What you're trying to say is that you've never been anywhere quite like this before and find it a bit overwhelming.'

'Well . . .'

He ignored her hesitation, obviously believing she sought to hide she hadn't known such places existed, apart from perhaps photographs in fashionable magazines. 'You'll soon get used to this sort of thing. Girls like you don't remain innocent for ever.'

'Mr Fenwick!' she protested.

'Don't worry, Sara,' he smiled smoothly, 'it's not that kind of place. The decor might be a little suggestive, if that's how you would describe Neptune rising out of the sea with little on, but that's as far as they go here. The very young cut their teeth on this sort of thing, so I thought it might be as good a place for you to begin as any.'

CHAPTER THREE

SARA, feeling a sudden warmth of nervousness, undid the two top buttons of her blouse, exposing inadvertently the lines of her smooth, slender throat. 'Begin what, Mr Fenwick?' she frowned.

He sighed, apparently losing interest as the waiter passed them each a menu. 'I've only known you a few hours, Sara, but already I'm beginning to wonder if you're actually as innocent as you sound.'

The menu was printed in both French and English and was extremely long. Sara kept her eyes on the elaborately decorated pages. 'A girl can know about things and still be innocent,' she retorted quietly. 'It shouldn't be a subject for mockery, anyway.'

'Not if it's genuine,' he agreed neatly. 'It's usually one of the first things a man wonders about a girl.'

'I didn't realise it was so important,' she returned sharply, feeling he had no right to be trampling so sardonically over what she considered hallowed ground. He had no cause, she almost said, to be talking to her this way at all, yet she couldn't deny a certain excitement. Mark Fenwick made her too aware of herself—or him, she wasn't sure which, and she wasn't altogether sure she enjoyed the sensation.

His mouth quirked although she thought his eyes contained a trace of interest as he glanced at her. 'Calm down, Sara, it's only a kind of game. Some questions need not be direct, nor do the answers. Not until people really get to know each other, then it can be important.'

Behind his light words seemed to lie a vague threat, as if he was warning her she couldn't hope to evade him indefinitely. That there would come a day of reckoning when he would be satisfied with nothing less than the truth.

Hastily Sara tried to thrust such an impression from her, reminding herself that it was ridiculous to be thinking like this about Mark Fenwick who, as managing director, was miles above her and whom she had only just met. Theirs could never be a normal friendship.

He turned his attention to the menu again, evidently not expecting a reply to his enigmatic comment, and, as Sara had eaten very little lunch and no tea, she was quite willing to start with the substantial soup he suggested. This was followed by poulet basquais for her and fillet of beef à l'indienne for himself.

'Do you enjoy living in your hostel, Sara?' You told me everything but that.'

Sara raised her head sharply, embarrassed suddenly to see he noted with a slight amusement the way she was enjoying her meal. 'Not very much,' she confessed, carefully laying down her fork, 'but I am trying to find a room.'

His amusement seemed to fade as his alert grey eyes watched her. 'Do you think that's a good idea?'

'Well, one has more freedom,' she began, trying to think of reasons other than the obvious.

'Freedom for what?'

She hesitated. 'I would be able to come and go as I pleased.'

'So you can have a nice cosy affair with this boy-friend you mentioned earlier?'

'Not everyone wants that sort of thing.'

'Most do, sooner or later,' he said dryly.

'Do you?' It was out before she stopped to think whom she was challenging. Feeling hot colour flooding beneath her skin, she muttered quickly that she was sorry.

He seemed more amused than annoyed, and, unlike herself, not at all confused. 'I believe I'm old enough to know what I'm doing.'

Sara swallowed, forcing herself to concentrate on her meal again, anything to escape looking directly at him. Yet something about his eyes seemed to draw her in spite of all her efforts to look away. Horrified, she found herself think-ing it might be no penance to gaze into them for ever. Even when he glanced at her casually it was as if she had been touched by something unforgettable.

'Haven't you ever wanted an affair with a man?' he went on, with the knack he had of making something slightly outrageous seem like normal conversation.

Rather desperately Sara clenched her hands under the table to try and stop herself shivering. 'Not yet,' she an-swered weakly, wondering why all kinds of insane possi-bilities should be flitting absurdly through her apparently unbalanced mind. If it was a sudden temptation to wonder what it would be like to have such a relationship with Mark Fenwick, it wasn't one to be contemplated seriously. As her eyes met his she felt further humiliated to realise he was perfectly aware of at least some of her thoughts.

The faintly sensuous curve of his hard mouth deepened. 'It gets easier after the first time, Sara.'

She was silent; only her fingers entwining tighter might have given a clue to her feelings, but he couldn't see them.

'No proper answer to that, either, Sara?'

She wished, with a resentful quirk, that he wouldn't make so free with her name. It was probably just another trick he had to make it seem he liked the sound of it. Defensively she tilted her chin. 'My only possible answer might jeo-pardise my job.'

'Uh,' his grin was diabolical, as he placed his elbows on the table and leant nearer, 'as bad as that, is it? So I'm left to read between the lines.'

'No doubt you're something of an expert, Mr Fenwick.'

'How prim you sound, Sara!'

She didn't feel so prim, not when he was very near to her like this.

'And how sexy you look,' he added, his voice low and sur-prisingly serious. 'It's a direct contradiction.'

She stared at him, her eyes widening, unable to look away. He might have been making actual love to her; her response might have been little different in his arms. Her pulse quickened and there was heat as well as colour in her cheeks. She was only of average height and very slender, but her figure curved and was extremely well rounded in the right places, only never before had any man made her so aware of it. Mark Fenwick made her feel curious about things she hadn't consciously given much thought to previously. They were strangers, but there was something almost tangible between them, a spark of peculiar electricity as their eyes met, which frightened even while it called insistently for further exploration!

Such impressions seemed to burn and Sara shrank nervously away from them, but her voice was slightly breathless. 'I don't have to admit anything of what you say, Mr Fenwick. Anyway, my mind would always triumph over matter.'

'How very young you sound!' His mouth twisted cynically. 'You'd be willing to bet?'

About to say yes, she hesitated, her heart beating so fast she wasn't sure she could say so truthfully. Instead she lowered her shining head and said modestly, 'I don't bet, I'm afraid.'

'No?' His eyes studied the small intense face opposite, the mouth which was sensuously curved and enticing. 'People who aren't willing to take even this kind of wager are usually very unsure of themselves.'

Uncertainly Sara frowned down at her empty sweet dish, not wanting to admit that he could be near the truth. She still wasn't sure that she'd been wise in allowing him to bring her here. Reminding herself that he had openly acknowledged that he was seeking a scapegoat, she judged from his remarks that he was getting his money's worth. She only wished it didn't seem to hurt so much that he should regard her merely in this light.

She raised her eyes, her expression so serious that he reached across and gently took her hand. Her own tensed with the unexpected contact, then relaxed slowly as his fingers moved persuasively over the smooth, pale skin. 'You've probably had a rough time,' he said reflectively, catching her eyes and holding them softly. 'Poor Sara. Where did you live in Coventry? In digs?'

'No, I lived with my aunt and uncle.'

'Why did you leave? Didn't they want you any more?'

The movement of his fingers was sympathetic but was paralysing her ability to think clearly, yet she was loath to take her hand away. 'I—it wasn't that at all. I just felt somehow I must escape.'

'So you decided to come to London?'

'Something like that.'

His eyes narrowed, as if he was convinced she hadn't told the whole story, while an oddly breakable look about her appeared to make him accept it—for the time being. 'How do you like working for Astro Chemicals, Sara?'

'Very much, thank you.'

He grinned suddenly, the unkindness back in his face. 'You sound about ten years old when you speak like that. Haven't we helped you grow up any? Doesn't the talk you are bound to hear shrivel every childish illusion? Haven't you heard any gossip about me yet? I don't suppose I'm immune.'

If only he knew! 'I don't listen to everything,' she assured him soberly. 'I mean, you're bound to be talked about a lot, seeing how ...'

'Yes?' he prompted softly, obviously not beyond a normal curiosity. Nor a touch of masculine vanity!

'Because of your position,' she said quickly, refusing to pander to him.

He retorted wryly, as if he guessed, 'I asked what was said. I quite realise why. I suppose it's a great pity I haven't a wife. Marriage might place me beyond such flights of speculation.'

'Only if you loved her and were faithful.'

One dark brow lifted. 'You sound as if this wasn't possible?'

Carefully, trying to control the faster beat of her heart which she feared he might feel through the thumb he held gently against her pulse, she said gravely, 'You would probably find it hard to fit a wife in with your busy life.'

He frowned, his eyes concentrated on her mobile mouth which he seemed to find intriguing. 'In other words, you think I wouldn't find her convenient?'

Without pausing to wonder at her own temerity, Sara nodded. 'Probably not.'

He said nothing for a moment, then his wide shoulders lifted ruefully. 'Perhaps you're right, Sara. I must admit I find a more casual relationship less trouble. I expect,' he added, with a challenging quirk, 'you don't approve.'

'No, Mr Fenwick,' she agreed soberly, 'I don't.'

'Why, you . . .' he looked as if he was about to indulge in a minor explosion but with a swift glance at his watch changed his mind. His brows drew together as if he was surprised and a little startled to find how time had flown. 'I'm afraid I must get you back to your hostel, Sara, and save any reprimands for another night. You wouldn't want to be locked out?'

'Oh, no!' As surprised as he to discover they had been here almost three hours, she scrambled to her feet. He had released her hand and she felt suddenly isolated again. 'I didn't realise,' she stammered.

'Neither did I,' he smiled, then paused to say gently, 'If you were locked out I might have to offer you a bed as well as a meal, and you wouldn't enjoy that as much, would you, Sara?'

He dropped her outside the hostel half an hour later. Standing beside the car, he pressed a note quietly into her hand. 'You'd better have this,' he said, 'until pay day or until your bag turns up. You don't need to thank me as you can always pay me back.'

Next morning Sara tried to borrow the money to do so immediately, but was unsuccessful. The girl in the room next door had only enough to last the next couple of days herself. She had news for Sara, though, which she seemed to think more important. She believed she had found a flat.

'It will only be small,' she announced, 'a bedroom and sitting room, but it could be going cheap. Would you come and look at it?'

'Yes—yes, of course.'

'You don't sound very thrilled?'

Sara felt too worried about her handbag to concentrate on anything else. 'I'm sorry,' she apologised. 'Yes, I'll come and look when I can manage. It will be good to get away from here.'

'We'll be able to have fellows in, and all that!' Delia, who had a good job in one of the large stores, hissed jubilantly, unperturbed by Sara's startled expression as she fled down the stairs to chase her bus. A second later she was out of sight, before Sara could ask exactly what she meant by—fellows. About to tell herself it didn't matter, she heard Mark Fenwick's taunting words and felt a little shiver of apprehension.

All that morning she found it impossible to settle because of her missing bag. No one had seen anything of it in the office where she worked and, as it didn't seem to dawn on anyone that she could have lost it during her lunch hour the day before, Sara didn't say anything. She was too terrified the grapevine had got to hear of Mr Fenwick taking her out. If Gwen or Miss Gregg suspected she had gone back to look for her bag last night she might never hear the last of it, and as Miss Drew hadn't contacted her about it, it seemed unlikely she had left it up there after all.

Today, at lunch time, she made do with a five-p packet of biscuits in the park. She still had most of Mark Fenwick's ten pounds but was unable to bring herself to spend any more than was absolutely necessary. The money seemed to burn a hole in her pocket and she wished fervently that he had never taken it upon himself to be so generous. She looked forward to paying him back, but somehow not to seeing him again. Whenever she thought of him, and this was too often, a quiver ran through her, frightening in its intensity. The best thing she could do after she was paid, she decided, was to leave the ten pounds with Miss Drew in a sealed envelope.

Because she had so little to eat she was back in the office with time to spare and spent it sitting brooding at her desk. When the telephone rang she felt singularly glad of the interruption and, as there was no one else there, picked it up. To her surprise it was Dicky, although he didn't say who it was until after he had asked for Miss Shaw and Sara informed him that he was speaking to her. He wanted to take her out that evening, and she felt rather ashamed to find herself relieved she had an excuse not to go.

'I'm sorry, Dicky,' she said, 'but I promised another girl I'd go with her to look over a flat.' Put that way the flat sounded grander than she suspected it was, but she could see no sense in going into lengthy explanations.

'Oh, damn,' she heard him mutter softly under his breath. He seemed really fed up.

'Another time, perhaps,' Sara consoled him hastily, not eager to make a more definite arrangement while wondering why he had suddenly lost the little charm he held for her.

After he had hung up she felt slightly ashamed, knowing she had been grateful enough for his company once and wishing bitterly that she didn't feel Mark Fenwick had something indirectly to do with it.

It was after five, when everyone was packing up for the night, when Miss Gregg called from the other side of the room, 'Sara, you're wanted in Mr Fenwick's office.'

There followed a general chorus, 'Why on earth should you, of all people, be wanted there?'

'How should I know?' Sara bent on the pretext of adjusting the patent strap on her shoe in order to hide her confused face.

'Have you been up to something?'

'Of course not.' Without looking at anyone directly again she rushed out, breathing a sigh of relief that she didn't have to come back as she already had her coat on. By to-morrow they might have forgotten.

She was convinced such an abrupt summons could only mean her handbag had been found, though why this should happen so late in the day puzzled her. She could have told the others what it was all about, she realised to make a mystery out of it would only make them more curious, yet she felt she must make sure it was about her handbag before she said anything.

A few minutes later she was knocking once again on Mark Fenwick's door and almost as if he had been waiting specially she heard him request her to come in. When she did she found him standing beside his desk, his eyes hard but otherwise expressionless. Of Miss Drew there was no sign. She must have gone.

'You wished to see me, Mr Fenwick?' It was maybe her place to wait until he spoke first, but her inner tension was such that she couldn't seem to take too much of his silent surveillance.

'Yes, I did want to see you!'

Was it her imagination or did each word really fall like a silky threat on her unfortunate head?

He waited for her to come forward, his grey eyes enigmatical on her slender, graceful figure, her uncertain face. When she was near enough he said coolly, 'Your handbag has been found.'

'Oh, good!' She was so relieved that now she would be able to return his money, she smiled happily, forgetting his unfriendly demeanour. Without waiting she began scrambling in her pockets for notes, bringing out nine in all, laying them, with a lot of small change, on his desk. 'I think I've spent ...' she paused, doing a swift calculation of bus fares and biscuits. 'I thought my bag must be somewhere,' she murmured absently, as she arrived at the correct sum.

'You mean you knew it would be here all the time!' His glance was flinty and he seemed far from impressed by the prompt return of his money. If anything he looked contemptuous.

'Well, I——' nervously she hesitated, stopping to look up irresolutely at his forbidding expression. Her voice faltered. 'I didn't really think it could be anywhere else.'

'And I should have known it couldn't be,' he exclaimed sarcastically.

'But——' Sara began, floundering before what seemed like an all out attack. There was something here she didn't understand. He looked as though he might easily despise her? 'Mr Fenwick,' she choked, wondering if he would notice she was unable to utter more than his name.

If he did he ignored it, so keen did he appear to berate her. 'Last night your seemingly stricken reaction over your lost handbag must have rendered me temporarily insane. You told me you'd looked everywhere, yet I found it this morning under the very chair you swore you'd looked under! Where a blind person might have found it!'

Sara, frozen slowly by waves of shock, stood staring up at him. Her face went pale and she was conscious of feeling very cold, of her heart beating too rapidly. Surely he didn't think she had deliberately pretended it wasn't there? That she had planned such a complicated sequence of events in order to extract an invitation to dinner? Apprehensively her distracted gaze searched his face and she was aware of a sinking feeling. This wasn't the same man who had been kind to her, who had held her hand in such an intimately comforting manner.

'You seem quite convinced of this.' Her voice shook, it seemed a miracle she was able to speak at all.

'I'm quite convinced,' he said harshly, his lips twisting with a smouldering anger.

'I see.' The effort to look straight at him while he glared at her like this proved too much. Helplessly she lowered her anguished eyes, shaking her head. 'I can't do more than assure you I did look under that chair. If my bag had been there last night I couldn't have missed it.'

He went on, as if she had never spoken, 'You can congratulate yourself that I fell completely for your story. For a while I thought you were young and sweetly innocent, but girls aren't any more, are they! From the cradle upwards they practise the art of fooling their opposite sex. Can you wonder men are so cynical? I felt sorry for you, Sara, and you couldn't take advantage of my sympathy fast enough.'

Which wasn't exactly correct, as he hadn't said he was taking her out entirely for her own sake? Someone to niggle at—if she remembered rightly! He wasn't being fair. While he might have every reason to be suspicious, he didn't even give her the benefit of the doubt. Of course a man in his position wouldn't need to worry over-much as to whether he was being absolutely fair or not. Nor, she reflected, suddenly puzzled, would he need to lie about anything. If he had really found her handbag where he said he had, if she protested too much, judging by the mood he was in, she might easily lose her job.

'I'm sorry, Mr Fenwick,' she mumbled, her eyes filling with confused tears as she hastily scrubbed her pride through the dust. 'You really have got this wrong but I'm sorry for all the trouble I've caused you.'

Her feeble apology, far from soothing, only seemed to infuriate further. 'I'm not used to people taking advantage of me, Miss Shaw! I might listen if I thought they were speaking the truth, but you're nothing but a grasping little typist.'

'No, please. . . !'

He grasped her shoulders, then, as if he couldn't restrain himself, his biting fingers choking off her stumbling words, 'What exactly were you after, Sara? You certainly aim high enough!'

Cautiously, feeling about to faint, she licked her dry lips, but before she could gather a reply he went on ruthlessly, 'Didn't you think you'd be a bit out of your depth with me?'

'I wasn't even thinking about anything like that!'

His eyes gleamed with contempt. 'Not even what you might get out of me? I must confess you had me interested.'

'I can't believe you'd be interested in a girl like me. Not —not romantically, if that's what you mean?'

'What other way would I be interested in you? Maybe I wouldn't have taken you out if you didn't possess a pretty face and enticing figure, but that's as far as it went, Miss Shaw, and a lot further than I intended to go.'

Drowning in a flood of resentment, Sara forgot the need to be cautious. 'I think you're despicable!'

'Why? You might have had reason for complaint if I'd asked you to sleep with me. Or are you disappointed I didn't?'

They were talking quickly to each other, but while his eyes were narrowed and insulting, hers were wide, darkening with nervous tension as his words and the trauma of emotion they seemed to arouse went spinning through her. His hands still held her shoulders in an iron-like grip and when she tried to struggle free of them they only dug deeper. 'I don't think you realise,' she gasped, 'what you're saying or doing!'

'Nothing you don't deserve.'

His dark, hard face seemed cold with anger and Sara felt that to say more might simply make matters worse. His temper, when aroused, was not exactly a secret and she had no wish to bear the full brunt of it. Silently she stared up at him as if defying him to do or say anything more. She wasn't aware that her expression changed from fright to defiance again, infuriating him further.

Furiously he jerked her to him and before she could draw back his head bent and she felt the quick force of his lips. He kissed her, and it was harsh and hurting, as no doubt he intended it should be. His mouth was experienced and brutal, a kind of punishment, all the more frightening for being so spontaneous. Sara might have been grateful if she'd felt nothing, but her nerves shattered instantaneously before the shafts of forked lightning which seemed to tear right through her. He wanted her to suffer; a hundred years ago or more he might have taken a whip to her, but today, momentarily, he could think of no worse punishment than to inflict the cruel penalty of his mouth. Sara sensed this even through the stunned and shattered state of her mind.

Mark must have intended his assault to be brief, merely an immediate, effective reprisal, but when she tried to break away his arms slid firmly around her slender back and tightened. He held her closer, but his mouth eased a fraction as if to allow her to draw a tortured breath. Then almost at once his lips crushed down again, cruelly into the trembling softness of hers. She couldn't move, she didn't really know, once she stopped struggling, if she actually wanted to, but she couldn't have done had she tried. She felt as if she must faint or cry out with the strangeness and excitement of his rough embrace, but it seemed she couldn't put up any more resistance. There seemed no end to it, the way he held her, the infliction of something more overwhelming than punishment which was rendering her slowly helpless, even responsive—but suddenly, when she least expected it, she was free.

Abruptly he released her, holding her automatically when she might have fallen, but his hands now those of an uninterested stranger. 'That might prevent you from trying to play games which are too adult for you. It might break you of the habit before you become endangered.'

She pressed a shaken hand against her raw lips as the whole world revolved dizzily. Wildly she wondered how he could look so remote, so composed. His eyes as they watched her feeble efforts at control were hooded, enigmatic, giving nothing away.

His coldness seemed worse to Sara than anger. The force of feeling within her was so chaotic her control was slipping. She would liked to have screamed, to hit out at his hard, cynical face, yet her strength seemed suddenly to leave her and she could only stare at him dazedly, her breath tearing great holes in her lungs.

She heard him mutter something she couldn't make out, but when he spoke again it wasn't under his breath. He sounded as if his control was only fractional. 'You'd better take your bag and go!' He held it out to her as his hands left her arms and, looking at it numbly, Sara wondered how such a pathetically shabby object could have been the cause of so much trouble.

Bravely she tried to look straight at him, but her wavering glance rose no higher than the cleft of his chin. Swiftly she grabbed her bag, scarcely aware of what she was doing. 'Thank you,' she whispered, her lips so bruised from the assault of his mouth that she could say no more. Without waiting for another comment she turned and fled.

For the next week Sara felt only half alive and though she was aware that her confrontation with Mark Fenwick had a lot to do with it she kept telling herself she was foolish to let it affect her so. It wasn't as if he would ever spare her another thought. Not that she wanted him to. If that had been a sample of how he treated women then she was better off without him!

In the office, next morning, she had confessed frankly about losing her handbag and how it had been found again. While not going into any details, she was glad she had told the truth as, after a few vaguely disappointed remarks, no one said anything more. As she had hoped, they appeared to assume Miss Drew had dealt with the matter herself, and dismissed the whole episode in favour of something more interesting. What they might have said had they known of Sara being in Mark Fenwick's arms didn't bear thinking about!

It seemed only a kind of anticlimax, nothing to penetrate her dull apathy, when Gwen and she almost stumbled across his path as they went to lunch. If he saw either of them he gave no indication as they paused to allow him to pass. After her first startled glance into his eyes, Sara's gaze fell from his tall, grey-suited figure, but this still didn't prevent her staring after him. The set of his dark head and wide shoulders made a pulse jerk at the base of her throat and her skin burned as she recalled how his mouth had dealt with her own. Inadvertently her face went white, and Gwen asked if she was all right. Fortunately she didn't seem to connect it with Mark! She did talk about him, though, much to Sara's despair, rambling on about his devastating good looks and how he was supposed to be going away for the rest of the week. Sara felt only relief.

About the office, of course, there was no avoiding the talk, which continued to buzz. Mark was on his way to Belgium, after this to Rome before flying to Venezuela to attend a Trade Exhibition in Caracas. From there he would probably return home. Miss Drew had gone with him this time, but it was rumoured she would come back after Rome. The other girls sighed loudly and said what a pity it was that Miss Drew was so very old. She must be fiftyish, if she was a day, it was such a waste!

The flat which Sara's friend at the hostel was after was let to someone else who had got there quicker, so, having nothing particular to do, Sara spent the following Saturday with Gwen in the West End. She felt rather guilty about this as she knew she should be looking for another flat, but somehow she seemed to have lost her enthusiasm. Nor did she feel very keen to tour the big stores with Gwen, but it was something to do. The winter day was cold and rashly she bought a woolly coat with a huge fluffy hood from a bargain rail. It was well marked down, perhaps because it was white, but it suited Sara's distinctive colouring to perfection. Gwen laughed and told her she looked good in it and just ready for the country. This made Sara think immediately and nostalgically of the large country cottage where she and her parents had lived outside Oxford, because it had been handy for the University. She wished she had been in the country today, chopping wood for their huge log fires with her father. London was nice, she might even enjoy it, if only she could escape sometimes at weekends. She supposed she could have gone to Coventry for weekends, but it was still a city and her aunt and uncle were always so busy.

She hadn't seen Dicky Gordon for over a week and felt so ashamed to realise she had scarcely given him a thought that she agreed to go out with him the next time he asked her. He, in fact, reminded her that she had refused the last time and she didn't like to do so again. Anyway, she had nothing else to do. The outing wasn't altogether a success, which didn't really surprise Sara as so few of her evenings with Dicky were. Looking back, she realised they were both too often occupied with their own thoughts and that there was unfortunately no spark of mutual attraction between them, or so it seemed to Sara. Rather uneasily she wondered what it was that had made her agree to go out with him in the first place. She had to remind herself that everyone needed a friend. Dicky had told her how lonely he was, and she had been feeling that way herself when she had first bumped into him. Their association did not necessarily have to be a romantic one. That evening they saw a film as usual, then had a light meal during which they talked of various things but nothing of any importance. Certainly Dicky was not inclined to mention his work or his private life, but as Sara wasn't very curious this didn't seem to matter. He said he would be in touch as he lightly kissed her goodnight, but he made no definite arrangement.

When it became common knowledge that Mark Fenwick was back, Sara's heart plummeted. She had imagined she felt much better while he was away. Now she began to worry all over again. She tried to convince herself that if she was careful she needn't so much as catch sight of him, and to fear he might get her dismissed because of her past sins was probably foolish. Yet for all her sensible conclusions even to know he was in the same building had an adverse effect. Her work suffered, she made trivial mistakes which annoyed Miss Gregg more than big ones might have done. This afternoon she had spelt two words the wrong way around and quoted pence instead of pounds on an account sheet. Miss Gregg's remarks had naturally been scathing, and now something else had happened to upset her.

'You're wanted in head office again, young Sara.' She put down the intercom just as they were all packing up for the day. She emphasised the 'again' with an impatient sigh. 'I really can't think what you've been up to this time!'

'You're sure it's me?' Sara gasped distractedly, hoping that if it was the floor might open and swallow her up.

'We don't have two of you!' Miss Gregg's dryness was far from flattering.

Sara, lifting her rounded chin, tidied her desk numbly and went, trying to maintain a dignified front but fearing she failed dismally.

What could Mark Fenwick want to see her about this time, if it was Mark who wanted to see her? She doubted it would be his secretary. Could it be he intended to dismiss her? Perhaps, because he had acted so unconventionally, their last encounter bothered him. She could be—what was it, a thorn in the flesh until he got rid of her, and thanks to her own stupidity she had no real defence.

In this last assumption, however, Sara wasn't sure she was being absolutely fair to herself. Mark had accused her of all sorts of things, but she was still willing to swear her handbag hadn't been under that chair. And if she had made a mistake through being anxious and in a hurry, it hadn't been intentional. Never, she vowed fervently, would she ever forgive him the awful things he had said. Not, she thought bitterly, that he'd ever be likely to ask her to! Apparently not satisfied with what he had already said and done, he was about to castigate her even further with instant dismissal.

Convinced that things could not be worse and there was little point in grovelling, Sara failed to understand why she felt so odd. By the time she reached the top floor she could feel the now familiar trembling in her limbs, the way in which her pulse was hammering. Outside his office door she was forced to pause, using a nervous hand to smooth her fluffy hair, to rub from her hot brow a dampness of perspiration. Then the dark mystery of him seemed to reach out, catching hold of her imagination, forcing her to knock and walk in, after Miss Drew had acknowledged her timid tap.

Miss Drew was in the act of putting on her coat and turned a polite face towards her. 'Go right in—Miss Shaw, isn't it? I believe Mr Fenwick is expecting you.'

No curiosity was apparent in Miss Drew's veiled glance. She was too well trained for that, but this didn't stop Sara feeling extremely self-conscious. It took a huge effort to smile and say thank you and then to open the inner door, as if an interview with the managing director was, for someone like herself, no unusual thing.

CHAPTER FOUR

MARK FENWICK was on the telephone when she went in and, as he listened to his caller, he indicated with an abstracted wave of his hand that Sara should sit down. Quickly she did so, taking care to avoid the chair on which she had sat on that other fateful evening. She also took care, after a first swift glance, to avoid looking at him at all, making a determined effort to keep her eyes firmly fixed on the floor.

He continued his conversation but with his eyes on Sara all the time, as she sat scarcely daring to breathe. She heard Miss Drew leaving. After this there was only silence apart from the minutes when the whole room seemed filled with his deep, resonant voice. She tried to concentrate on the carpet, a soothing dark brown, but found her gaze sliding towards him, riveted magnetically. It made her pulse jerk to find he was watching her and a hot embarrassment flooded her pale cheeks. Instantly she looked away, wishing fervently that she had outgrown the infuriating habit of blushing like a schoolgirl, especially now she was almost nineteen!

He put down the phone at last and she saw his hand linger as if he considered it his last link with sanity. 'Well, can't you even bear to look at me?' he asked quite savagely.

'I ...' she stammered, not wholly understanding his question, 'I can't very well sit and stare at you. It might have been better if I'd waited outside until you'd finished.'

'Hmm, yes, I suppose you're right. But you still haven't answered my question directly.' His voice softened considerably though his eyes were still keen. 'I asked if you didn't like me any more.'

In view of what had happened, Sara thought he wasn't

being particularly fair. He must know that feelings couldn't be turned on or switched off like a machine. His attitude only seemed to add to the mystery of why he had sent for her in the first place. Surely he wasn't about to apologise for the way he had treated her last time? She blinked as she considered such a possibility. A man like Mark Fenwick wouldn't feel remorse for anything unless he was completely convinced he had been at fault and, in regard to her handbag, this didn't seem likely. Yet—her smooth brow pleating, Sara stared at him rather blindly; his words, his attitude would appear to suggest there was something. A wild hope stirred in her breast only to die a sudden death as her bewildered eyes met his and his expression changed harshly.

'Forget it,' he commanded curtly. 'I'm surprised myself that I can ask such a foolish question.'

'What did you want to see me about?' she asked quickly, before she could start pondering on that.

'Nor is that the sort of thing you should be asking,' he reproved impatiently. 'You're supposed to sit there and wait until I tell you. Certainly a girl in your position wouldn't be expected to take the initiative.'

If it hadn't been so crazy Sara might have suspected he was stalling for time, and it came to her suddenly that he might be finding it difficult to actually dismiss her when it came down to it. Well, she didn't want his pity, but neither would she make it easier for him by letting him know she understood what this was all about. She looked down again, giving all her attention to the carpet. 'I'm sorry,' was all she said.

'You don't look it, not particularly,' he retorted, his eyes narrowed on her downbent face. 'You asked what I wanted to see you about. You must surely have guessed it was your regrettable handbag? The one you're clutching even now so fiercely to your person.'

As she swallowed a numb surprise he continued, 'First of all I might tell you I am not amused by such a time-wasting and absurd sequence of events, in which I should never have involved myself in the first place! It almost convinces me, Miss Shaw, that I'm as susceptible to feminine wiles as the next man. Offering you coffee was my first mistake, giving you a meal my next. Jumping to the wrong conclusions my third, and something tells me that this, our fourth momentous encounter, might inadvertently turn out to be the biggest mistake of the lot.'

'Mr Fenwick...?'

She might never have spoken, nor did he hesitate over her startled expression. 'It appears I owe you an apology, Miss Shaw, if you'll hear me out!'

Suitably chastised, she lapsed into an uneasy silence, still scarcely able to believe the evidence of her own ears.

'Yes,' he leant forward, as if eager to judge the full effect of his words, 'Miss Drew has confessed she found your bag last week and locked it away.'

'I knew...!'

'Don't interrupt, Sara! If you remember I had a conference that afternoon after we first met. Miss Drew, I'm afraid, had no idea you'd been any further than the door of my office. She found your handbag much later and simply didn't connect it with you. She locked it safely away and unfortunately went home, forgetting about it. This is why it was still locked in her confounded cupboard and we couldn't find it. Next morning, however, my paragon of a secretary decided it must belong to one of my lady friends and, as I had never mentioned such a visit, obviously mustn't want her to know about it. Hence the unobtrusive way in which she returned it, exactly as she had found it, under your chair. It was, as you already know, the first thing I saw when I came in.'

Long before he came to the end of it Sara felt almost sick with a kind of nervous tension. By the time he stopped her eyes were riveted widely on his steely face. 'So this is why you thought...?'

'Exactly,' his mouth relaxed ruefully. 'I can see, Sara, you aren't sure whether to be relieved or angry.'

'Maybe you'll only allow me to be the former,' she replied bitterly. She took a deep breath, not seeing his wry expression. 'It doesn't seem like Miss Drew, somehow, does it? I mean, she doesn't seem the kind of person to go to such silly lengths?'

'It merely proves that even the Miss Drews of this world can make mistakes,' he rejoined mildly, evidently more inclined to be tolerant of Miss Drew than he had been of Miss Shaw!

Sara sensing this, resented it, even as she told herself it was to be expected, Miss Drew being such an old and treasured employee. She tried to lapse into her former dignified silence, but failed regrettably. The question was out before she could stop it. 'How did you find out about this?'

Mark smiled slightly. 'I found out when we were in Rome. Apparently, when I never mentioned the handbag, she had been contrarily apprehensive and, after she'd imbibed enough champagne at a business reception, it all came out. For several reasons, I might say, I wasn't too pleased.'

Was one of the reasons that he regretted getting mad and kissing her? Sara lowered her too revealing gaze lest he should guess what she was thinking. The thought of her handbag intruding in this way on such an important occasion struck her suddenly as being rather funny, and amusement showed briefly on her pale face.

'It wasn't particularly amusing,' he reproved, his grey eyes glinting as he caught the faint sparkle in her blue ones.

'I don't suppose it was, not very,' she agreed, the captivating curve of her soft lips uncertain again.

'Sara——' he began.

But it was Sara's turn to cut in. 'I hope you didn't frighten Miss Drew? You do rather frighten people sometimes.'

To her surprise, just as she shrank from her own astonishing imprudence, he nodded almost humbly. 'I don't intend to—well, not always,' he added with a wry grin. 'It's just part of the executive image. A little confident bullying, a bit of charm will often succeed where all else fails. Miss Drew understands me too well to be really afraid, I suspect.'

No doubt he used the same tactics on all women with much the same success. Sara frowned. In all fairness, she conceded he wouldn't be where he was today if he didn't have, and know, exactly the right methods. 'I see,' she murmured uncertainly, stilling a sharper response, not wishing to quarrel with him again. not even sure she could afford to!

'Sara——' He rose and came around to her side of the desk, perfectly aware of her young indignation and perhaps her reasons for restraining it. He took hold of her hands and drew her gently to her feet. 'What happened might not have been wholly my fault, but I apologise and hope you will forgive me?'

'Yes, of course, Mr Fenwick.'

His sigh went deep, his slight smile fading. He said tersely, 'Can't you do better than that, Sara?'

Colour came and went in Sara's face as she started in confusion and tried to release her hands from his. It couldn't matter all that much to him, but she had a feeling he didn't care to be denied anything, not even the forgiveness of a humble typist. She tried to compose herself, but it wasn't easy, possibly because of his towering nearness, his apparent determination to hold on to her hands. 'I don't know what you expect me to say,' she protested feebly. 'I find it difficult to believe you really believe me at last.'

He said confidently and coolly, allowing fractionally that she might have some small cause for complaint, 'I can't truthfully say I regret what happened, only the manner perhaps in which it did. I think we could improve on that.'

She marvelled at his arrogant audacity. Yet she felt herself softening, giving him, she supposed, the impression that she was extremely malleable. To correct this she said primly, 'I don't think you need say any more, Mr Fenwick.

I understand everything, now you've explained. It really isn't necessary for you to bother any further. Last week you lost your temper, but this, too, I can understand, being able to guess what a busy life you must lead.'

'Sara!' His impatience was back again, held only thinly in check. Then suddenly he smiled, his glance almost caressing. 'I want you to forget it all and promise to have dinner with me one evening. A proper night out this time. Not something rushed and rather furtive.'

Feeling altogether trapped, as much by her own urgent longing as anything, Sara glanced at him unhappily. 'I accept your apology, Mr Fenwick, you don't have to take me out as well.'

'But you must prove you forgive me.'

'You can't want to spend another boring evening, surely?'

'Miss Shaw!' his mouth tightened menacingly, 'are you turning yourself into a coy little compliment-seeker? I refuse to decide whether I was bored or not. I only know I have a fancy to repeat the occasion. I would appreciate a straight yes or no. I refuse to give you time to think about it!'

Sara blinked, as he obviously intended her to. How dearly she would have liked to have the courage to refuse such brusque determination, but it seemed she couldn't deny herself either—not completely. It was as if he held out something she couldn't resist, though she couldn't see what it was, not clearly. The strange clamouring of her senses seemed to warn rather than entice, but she ignored them. It was certainly nothing like what she felt when she was out with Dicky Gordon. He reminded her of a small boy seeking comfort. Mark Fenwick did not. Dicky she forgot almost before he was out of sight, whereas Mark Fenwick seemed to be with her all the time, only she had just realised it. 'Yes,' she whispered, groping desperately for a little confidence, 'I'll come, especially as you make it sound very like an order. I hope, Mr Fenwick, you enjoy yourself!'

'See that I do and I might forgive you that little note of sarcasm.' His eyes went over her consideringly. 'Do you still live in your hostel?'

She nodded.

'Good, then,' he said briefly, to her utter astonishment dropping a swift kiss on her soft red mouth before releasing her hands. 'You may go now, Miss Shaw, while I get on with some work. I'll pick you up at seven o'clock tomorrow evening—and don't keep me waiting.'

Looking back, it had often surprised Sara to recall how quickly she had slipped into an easy friendship with Mark Fenwick. It wasn't all that easy, but at least she didn't feel so nervous of him any more. The following evening was the first of many such occasions when he picked her up at the hostel and took her on somewhere for dinner. At first, on realising he never dropped her off without arranging to see her again, she had tried to wriggle out of further commitments, but he would have none of it.

'Would you rather I rang Miss Gregg and asked to speak to you during office hours?' he taunted. 'I'd be very willing to oblige, if only for the pleasure of taking some of the wind out of that particular lady's sails, but I doubt if it would make your life easier.'

Sara might have smiled at his indirect summing up of poor Miss Gregg's character if she hadn't felt so agitated by his last reference. Not that he had any need to put it into words. She always shrank from the possibility that one day her section might discover what had been going on and the talk it might cause. She had had a big enough task putting a vaguely innocent construction on her last visit upstairs—as they called it. If they were to suspect she went out with Mark Fenwick regularly, her life might not be worth living!

Why Mark should want to take her out fairly regularly she had no clear idea. He appeared to enjoy her company, but this didn't provide a very satisfactory explanation as he must know many women whose company he enjoyed as much as, if not more than, her own. As for herself, Sara soon found he was growing on her, like an addiction to strong wine. And strong wine he might prove to be, she suspected, unless she took him in very small doses! She knew, ruefully, even while his persistence puzzled her, that this wasn't the way she affected him. Sometimes when they were out he paid her little actual attention, apparently still absorbed with the more important events of the day. Then, again, when they did talk it was, more often than not, a lot about nothing. She found him, in his best moods, very easy to talk to. In many ways he was not unlike the men, both young and old, whom her father had brought frequently to their cottage, but at some point the similarity ceased. There was in Mark a more ruthless streak than that possessed by her more unworldly parents and their friends.

Mark never asked anything about her life before she had come to London. He knew nothing, apart from the little she had told him the very first time he had taken her out. If this did sometimes strike Sara as being rather strange, it also served as a warning that he in no way intended their present relationship to have any permanence. Quite clearly she was merely a sort of novelty of which he one day expected to tire. Yet when she resolved that because this was so obvious, she wouldn't see him again, she found herself giving in even more frequently to his increasing demands.

Sara liked it best when they dined in Mark's home, for all he teased her when she confessed as much, saying that at her age she should appreciate a more lively evening. He had what she thought a particularly beautiful home off Eaton Square, and she felt quite shocked when he said he was sometimes tempted to sell it and acquire a service flat.

'You wouldn't really, would you, Mark?' It had been Mark for some time now.

'No, I suppose not,' he smiled at her expression of startled disapproval. 'It belonged to my grandfather and I've never really thought seriously about selling. It does suit me, I must confess, as I do quite a lot of entertaining.'

'I expect you do.' Gazing wistfully around his charming

lounge on her first visit, Sara had felt suddenly flat.

'I have to, silly,' he had smiled comprehendingly. 'Business.'

'Oh, I see.' She hadn't tried to hide an inexplicable relief. 'You're lucky, anyway, to have inherited this.'

If he had noticed how she had rushed to cover up her mistake he gave no indication, but she remembered how he stared at her broodingly. 'Lucky? Yes, I suppose I am, but one often also inherits responsibilities. Some I could well do without.'

He hadn't explained, and because he never seemed curious about her previous affairs she felt she couldn't ask too much about his and she let the moment pass. She met his housekeeper—not inherited, he assured her later with a grin, but a necessity in his present circumstances. Sara had smiled, turning her attention to an intriguingly carved wood figure, wishing she could share his undoubted approval of another woman.

After these dinners, when his housekeeper usually retired to her own flat for the remainder of the night, Mark often put on records and they would drink coffee while listening idly for an hour of two. These evenings seemed to grow more precious as time went by. Mark, though keeping his distance, seemed to enjoy her company and Sara couldn't deny she liked his. He didn't attempt to make love to her even when there was enough opportunity, but restricted himself to a goodnight kiss. Which usually, she was forced to admit to herself, had little passion in it, being much too casual to have any meaning at all. It might have suggested he had some affection for her, but she wasn't even sure about this. Sometimes, she thought, she was becoming a habit, someone he liked having around, and she only wished she could regard him in the same indifferent light.

She still saw Dicky, but just very occasionally, although he made some attempt to establish a more definite relationship. Sara, however, with her head if not her heart full of Mark, did not share his enthusiasm and gradually their

meetings tapered off. Now and again she had coffee with
him on Saturday mornings, but these meetings seemed so
unimportant she didn't mention them to Mark.

One evening Mark surprised her by asking if she would
care to visit his cottage with him at the weekend. 'I have a
small place which I think you would like,' he smiled. 'It's so
deep in the country I don't get down very often but,
fortunately, some obliging neighbours keep an eye on it for
me. I should like you to see it, Sara. I've a feeling you're
really a country girl at heart.'

Whether this was complimentary or not, she didn't pause
to consider. Her small face lit up. 'I'd love to,' she agreed
eagerly. 'That is,' she had added more cautiously, 'if we can
get there and back in one day?'

'Oh, Sara!' he had laughed, hugging her to him and saying he hadn't forgotten she was so old-fashioned. Held close
against him, she had found the now too rare experience so
breathtaking she didn't notice that he hadn't directly answered her question.

Happily she prepared for her outing, thinking what a long
way Mark and she had come since their first meeting. The
usually dreary weeks of January and February seemed to
have flown, now she could scarcely visualise a life without him, and while she was aware that it might be dangerous to think this way, she couldn't help it. Seeing Mark
regularly seemed to be changing her utterly so that occasionally she felt she did not recognise herself. Sometimes
she felt so different she was sure it must be visible from the
outside and was slightly astonished that no one noticed.

Now it was Saturday morning, almost ten o'clock, and
she was free for the weekend, waiting for Mark to pick her
up. Snow was falling steadily over the city and it was cold,
but, wrapped in her fleecy white coat which she hadn't yet
worn, she scarcely noticed. Mark arrived with minutes to
spare and looked approvingly at the very attractive picture
she made standing on the slushy white pavement with
snowflakes clinging to her long, sooty lashes. He said a brief

good morning as he got out of his large, luxurious car to stow her small case away in the back. He had advised her to bring something tough for walking in and something pretty to change into later on, and she had obliged. In fact the 'something pretty' had kept her absorbed for days and ended up with her plunging extravagantly, during a lunch hour, on a new pinky-red dress which the assistant assured her did fabulous things for her hair and complexion. All Sara hoped was that Mark would like it. This suddenly seemed terribly important.

As they left London Mark told her his cottage was in Hampshire, so they had quite a way to go. With luck they might be there for lunch, which he hoped she would be prepared to cook. 'I've brought some provisions,' he said, 'and we can always shop locally if you find I've missed anything out.'

Sara pushed her hood back from off her beautiful dark head. 'I'm not a very good cook, Mark,' she confessed, 'but I'll do my best.'

'You'd better!' he threatened. 'I'll be quite furious if the only thing I have to show for this weekend is a bout of indigestion!'

Sara laughed, not even then feeling alarmed. She refused to spoil her day by challenging the impression she had that he intended to make it longer. The road was new to her and she soon became absorbed, especially when they neared their destination and the maze of narrow lanes which constantly confused her. Mark then set out to convince her that he knew where they were better than she did and Sara argued that the map couldn't be wrong. By the time they reached the cottage he was chuckling with a deep amusement while she felt only cross.

The rutted lane, almost a half a mile in length, which led up to the cottage sobered him a little. 'I'll have to do something about this eventually,' he muttered, as the car slid into a pothole concealed by the still falling snow. He righted the slipping vehicle and sighed, 'If one wants isolation one can't have everything, I'm afraid. Sometimes, Sara, this place has just about saved my sanity. It's been an escape, a retreat. Somehow I don't want to spoil it with all the trappings of civilisation, not even a new road.'

Sara didn't interrupt. What he was saying astonished her. Somehow she had thought him beyond normal human weaknesses, but now that she could almost feel him relaxing she realised his life wasn't without strain. She smiled softly, and let him talk, saying nothing until they arrived.

She loved the cottage on sight. It stood back from the road on a slight rise. Framed by fir trees and with a thatched roof, it looked exactly like a Christmas card.

'Why, it's beautiful!' she breathed, leaning forward so that her small, straight nose almost touched the windscreen, her blue eyes shining.

'I said you'd like it,' Mark smiled, his glance resting on her with some satisfaction, 'only I didn't quite anticipate such admiration. I must make a note of it. Buy Sara a cottage for her birthday—she adores them.'

'Fool!' she laughed at him, not betraying that this reminded her of another, larger cottage where she had been born, but her eyes were unnaturally bright and she didn't see his narrow thoughtfully as she got out. 'Anyway,' she tacked on inanely, 'my birthday's past.'

'When?' he asked.

'Oh, about two weeks ago.' She wished she had never mentioned it.

'Did you get many presents?'

'None,' she shrugged carelessly. 'I had a card from my aunt.'

'Ah,' he said, obviously connecting her presentless state with her tears. 'Well, that might teach you not to keep your birthday a secret in future. You could have dropped a little word in my ear, but it's perhaps not too late to do something about it.'

Sighing, Sara turned towards the cottage again, feeling that to say more might only continue to exaggerate the thing out of all proportion, and it hadn't been her birthday which had caused a tear.

From the way Mark had talked she had expected the cottage to be rather tumbledown and ordinary, and she was thrilled to find it was neither. Inside it was a bit dark as the small windows let in very little light, but there was electricity. Mark told her he had installed this at great cost but it had proved invaluable when he arrived from London late at night, when other forms of heating and lighting would have been impracticable.

Before she began lunch he showed her around. The lounge was of medium size, cosy rather than smart, although Sara recognised that the deep chairs were expensive and the other furniture genuine antique. The floor was covered by a thick red carpet and a huge brick fireplace was piled high with logs. Mark bent down and put a match to it and she watched the yellow flames leap greedily among the dry wood.

'I don't have central heating in here.' He stood back from the roaring fire after pushing a log into place with his toe. 'There are radiators in the hall and other rooms, but I like to rely on a fire in here. I believe it adds to the atmosphere.'

There wasn't a separate dining room, but the kitchen was large and had a table in the centre big enough for casual meals. Upstairs there was only one bedroom, this containing a huge double bed.

'I like comfort, as you've no doubt gathered,' Mark said, noticing her interest in the otherwise spartan room.

'I was looking at the beams,' she retorted hastily, correcting, she hoped, any impression that she had been overinterested in the bed. The beams were indeed attractive, being old and knotted with a kind of ageless, gleaming patina which must defy the advancing years. Crouched above the low casement windows, they seemed to sweep Sara back into other centuries. What Mark said about the bed disturbed her, why, she wasn't sure, but it caused her to make another rather obvious remark. 'You only have the one bedroom?'

'Yes. Definitely not a house for entertaining in.' As they went out he ducked his tall head to avoid the low door. 'Do you know, you're the first visitor I've asked?'

What did he mean by that? It sounded enigmatic, as if there had been those who had just turned up, out of the blue.

The small landing was funny but endearing, with a bathroom on one side and the twisting stairs on the other. Sara's heart beat coldly for a moment, as she speculated unhappily on his 'other' visitors. She tried to pass Mark quickly, but instead of succeeding neatly she tripped and almost fell against him.

He caught her, taking the full weight of her slender body, his eyes glinting.

'I'm sorry!' she gasped, trying to free herself of his enclosing arms. 'I didn't do that on purpose.'

'Oh, Sara,' he laughed, planting a sudden, deep kiss on her tremulously parted lips, 'I know you didn't, but sometimes I wish you did.'

The feel of his mouth was still on hers, his breath, faintly smoky, still in her nostrils. Her eyes widened as he answered her startled, unspoken question. 'Haven't you ever deliberately set out to ensnare a man, Sara? A man doesn't feel so guilty if it happens that way.'

She frowned, the coldness of a minute ago back, knowing she was, as yet, too self-conscious to act as he implied. His suggestion bewildered her, seeming only to emphasise the difference in their real attitudes. The smart, sophisticated women he usually took out would undoubtedly be more than able to supply all the encouragement he seemed to miss. 'I'm sorry,' she answered at last, with a slight shake of her shining head.

With a remorse which seemed genuine he gave her a friendly hug which appeared to deny his brief flare of passion. 'Forgive me, Sara. I think I've grown too blasé.

Anyway,' he teased her downcast face, 'I daren't now ask what you think of my bed. Now that you're so disapproving!'

'I don't have time,' she smiled back as his humour affected her, 'to voice an opinion. It's either that or your lunch.'

His eyes were all over her sparkling face before slipping lower. 'What a choice to put before any man! You really believe I don't know which I want most?'

Laughing, she twisted nimbly to escape him, relieved that he couldn't feel how her heart was thudding with a hitherto unknown excitement. Mark made it seem like a game, but she sensed underneath his teasing a thread of seriousness. She found herself wondering wistfully what it would be like if he really cared? She could care for him, she realised, already suspecting she was more than a little in love with him and trembling as the full implication of this hit her. Hastily she ran down the stairs, deriving no comfort from the low, mocking laughter that followed her flying footsteps.

She cooked lunch for the two of them while he brought in her suitcase and more fuel for the fire. Then, tying a large apron around his waist, he set the table.

'You didn't know I was domesticated, did you, Miss Shaw?' he taunted, his eyes still retaining a hint of the contemplative gleam that had smouldered in them as he had followed her downstairs.

Pretending to concentrate on getting a succulent steak from the grill to their plates, she retorted primly, 'If you've come here a lot and looked after yourself you're bound to have learnt something.'

'You could say,' he nodded, glancing appreciatively at the large helping she passed him. 'I'm afraid I couldn't match your expertise. If this tastes as good as it looks I shall want you down here more often.'

'They do say the way to a man's——' Sara began blithely, then stopped, her cheeks flaming.

He smiled softly at her confused face. 'Did you set out to find your way to my heart, Sara?'

'Don't be silly,' she managed to collect herself and shrugged carelessly, 'it was just one of those things, a senseless remark.'

'I might take some convincing of that,' he teased, still smiling.

The snow stopped falling after lunch and Mark pointed out that his supply of wood was low. 'There's plenty of other fuel but no more logs. We could go into the copse and saw some, if you feel like it?' he suggested.

Sara, who hadn't seen a real fire for a long time, agreed eagerly. 'We must need some exercise, anyway, after sitting in the car so long,' she smiled.

'And after such a good lunch,' he regarded her quizzically, patting his flat stomach ruefully. 'I thought you said you couldn't cook?'

'My mother used to say I was a natural cook, only lacking in experience.'

'You mother must have been a very astute woman,' he said, walking over to lift two anoraks from a peg on the door. One he tossed to Sara. 'Your white coat is charming but not very suitable for wet trees and sawdust.'

The ground was white and hard under their feet and a light wind blew through the branches above their heads as they walked through the forest. Mark knew where an old tree had fallen during the autumn and there were still a few branches left. As they made their way towards it Sara marvelled at their complete isolation. She hadn't thought Hampshire could be so lonely. Mark told her his nearest neighbour was almost three miles away. Here there was nothing but trees and snow-covered undergrowth, broken only by an occasional stream. As a retreat it must be perfect, if not very practical for everyday living.

They found the wood and set about getting it home where Mark said it would be easier to deal with. He would only allow Sara to carry one small branch while he lifted two much larger ones on to his broad shoulders. Sometimes Sara found herself wondering at his tough, hard body. He had the look of a man who spent more time over physical pursuits than in an office, and again she was forced to admit that he was very attractive.

So busy was she gazing at him, breathing in the strength and breadth of him, that over a small stream she completely missed her footing and fell. She only wet one leg, but the cold was uncomfortable and she was glad she had something to change into when they reached the cottage again.

Mark grinned, and she thought he was hard-hearted because he didn't immediately put down his own load and help her rescue hers, which was floating down the swollen water. When she complained he merely told her she shouldn't walk along with her eyes closed, and for a few minutes she pretended a pained silence.

Altogether they passed a few pleasantly carefree hours fetching and chopping the wood and stacking it up, teasing each other lightly in between. Sara knew she was happy, happier than she had been for months, and while it might be a dangerous kind of delight she was human enough to decide rashly only to live for the moment. The shadows lengthened as the afternoon advanced. Soon they would have to return to London. There would just be time to wash and change, perhaps to make a pot of tea and a slice of toast on Mark's hot fire before they went. All this wood they had sawed was going to be surplus.

'We can't possibly use it up,' she reproached him, picking up a handful of snow, making it into a snowball which she threw at him in mock rage. 'It's right what they say in the office, you're a tyrant who just can't bear to see anyone idle!' Swiftly she made up another snowball as she missed with the first when he ducked. 'But let me tell you, Mark Fenwick, you'll have to pay! So much an hour for cooking your lunch, not to mention chopping your logs!'

This time she had a lucky shot which caught his shoulder, shooting snow up into his face. With mock ferocity he swooped down, snatching her up. 'You're getting much too confident, Miss Shaw! For such audacity towards your managing director the greater penalty will be yours—to pay later, when you get cleaned up. I refuse to get sawdust in my mouth, and your face, my darling child, is covered in it!'

He deposited her frantically struggling body in the kitchen as if she weighed no more than a feather, disregarding, with a sardonic face, her pink cheeks and sparkling eyes. When he let her go he was smiling, taking no notice of her trembling indignation. 'Your suitcase is behind you,' he informed her. 'You'd better take it upstairs and repair the damage while I carry in the logs. There's enough hot water.'

There was! The bathroom was now lovely and warm and Sara swiftly inserted the bath plug and ran the taps while removing her wet clothing. Wallowing in the water, which was deep and hot, she forgot all about the lengthening shadows. At the hostel, when she had a bath, there was always someone hammering at the door, and very rarely was there any hot water. Unless one was first it was usually only lukewarm.

So comfortable was she that she almost fell asleep. She might have done if the memory of Mark's arms, twice in the same afternoon, hadn't kept wakening her up with disturbing tremors. But he had also been kind, she reminded herself; it would be something to dream about on the way back to London. When they got back, she mused drowsily, her anxiousness of a few minutes ago almost forgotten, as her heavy eyelids closed.

CHAPTER FIVE

LATER Sara's heart thudded as she heard Mark knocking at the door.

'I've made some tea,' he called. 'Hurry up, lazybones!'

'I'll come right away,' she called back, remembering he would want to get home before it got too late.

When his footsteps faded she scrambled quickly from the bath and after drying herself on one of the huge towels, pulled the pinky-red dress which looked so gay over her curly brown head. The dress was made of a man-made fibre, as warm as wool but silky soft, and felt delightful against her skin. The effect, she noticed in the small bathroom mirror, was good. With fingers that shook slightly she applied a touch of matching lipstick and ran a swift comb through her still damp hair. This, she decided ruefully, standing on tiptoe to try and see herself better, would have to do as she had forgotten to bring anything else. Driving back, Mark would probably never notice whether she wore make-up or not and by the time they reached town it would be too late to go on anywhere for dinner.

As he had promised he had tea waiting when she got downstairs. He had brought it into the lounge which was now warm and cosy, with the fire burning brightly and the curtains snugly drawn against the cold. He rose to his feet when she came into the room, swiftly, as if he had been almost watching the door, and his eyes as they went over her were appreciative.

'Well worth waiting for,' he smiled, going forward and guiding her gently to a chair, immediately making her feel cherished. 'I like your dress, Sara.' His eyes lingered as though he enjoyed bringing a little colour to her cheeks. 'I wouldn't have imagined the colour right for you, with

77

your eyes such a definite blue, but it was a wise choice. It makes you look quite beautiful.'

Twice in the same day he had held her, twice had been unstinting in his admiration. She flicked him a bemused glance. 'It's new,' she confessed.

'And charming,' he smiled.

She pushed slim, suddenly nervous fingers through the hair which was curling softly about her slender neck and small ears. 'I hadn't much that seemed suitable for a snowy afternoon in the country,' she explained gravely.

His light grey eyes glinted. 'So you were really thinking of the weather, not me?'

'Of course,' she tried to make it sound convincing, for good measure meeting his amused eyes and adding with a daring severity, 'You're spoiled enough as it is.'

'Spoiled?'

Did his raised eyebrows have to speak so clearly of only mock alarm? 'By women, I mean,' she retorted.

'Sit down,' he growled, looking as if he almost enjoyed the slight push he gave her. 'You might not believe it, but you're talking nonsense. If any spoiling has been done it's been by me. You're different in this respect, Sara, you don't demand, as most other women of my acquaintance seem to do. No other woman has been willing to cook my lunch or help me saw wood.'

'Then you can't know the right kind.'

'Well, I do now,' he grinned lazily. 'It only proves, does it not, that it's never too late?'

She laughed lightly, as this seemed all she could do, and made a great thing of straightening her skirts. Then she held out her hands to the fire. At this, he said, 'Ah,' and passed her a long brass-handled toasting fork with a piece of bread on the end of it, and she was pleased that his taste for toast appeared to match hers exactly. The images of other women faded as she held the bread to a spot where the wood was red and glowing hotly. An odd sense of achievement overtook her as, after a few moments, the aroma of the browning bread began to invade the room, and she fell into a silent, dreamy mood which expressed itself in an audible, if unconscious, sigh of contentment.

Mark poured tea. It was hot and the toast tasted good. 'You took your time in the bath,' he said unexpectedly, as he sat by her side applying butter liberally.

Sara glanced at him quickly, remembering she hadn't asked if it was all right to take one. 'I'm sorry,' she apologised, 'I'm afraid I couldn't resist it.'

'I don't mind you having a dozen baths,' he replied wryly.

'I wouldn't want that many.' She tried to sound amused.

'Don't you have hot water in your hostel?'

'Not like this.' Her voice was wistful.

'So you see,' he teased, 'how right you were to come here after all.'

'Yes,' she met his eyes, her own glowing with swift, answering laughter, 'but I didn't come merely for a bath. I've enjoyed my day enormously, I only wish it had lasted longer. I suppose we must be leaving for London soon?'

Turning sideways in his chair, he gazed at her silently for a few contemplative moments before asking quietly, 'Do you really want to go back tonight, Sara?'

The unexpectedness of his low-voiced query travelled through her like a kind of shock, causing her breath to draw sharply. Was he actually asking if she would be willing to stay, or, in thinking so, was she applying the wrong construction? Surely he didn't imagine she was the sort of girl who made a habit of spending promiscuous weekends with men, weekends like some of the girls boasted of in the office? Was this what he had in mind? Surely not....

Sara's hand was shaking again and she refused to look at him as she carefully replaced her cup in its saucer. However fond Mark was of women, he wouldn't ask a girl like herself to spend that kind of weekend! In spite of his rather tantalising remarks he couldn't possibly want her to go to bed with him. Like herself he must have enjoyed the afternoon, the sympathetic companionship which seemed to have developed between them, and saw no real harm in prolonging their visit. It could be complimentary in a way, that he saw her as simply a friend, and mightn't she offend him irrevocably if she appeared to think otherwise? Might she not just make herself look foolish if she refused to stay —if this was what he really meant? It was tempting, she was ready to admit; the long journey back to London on a winter's night had little appeal.

She didn't realise how the silence had stretched until he stirred and said, 'You don't have to worry about a thing, Sara. We're both tired and in need of some relaxation. You can have the bed upstairs. I'll sleep down here.'

'Oh!' She felt so ridiculous, yet immediately relieved that a surge of singing happiness took the last of her tentative fears. She was aware that she still had a decision to make and was grateful that while Mark reassured he didn't try to over-persuade her. The choice, the final one, was hers, hers alone, but somehow, gazing around the lamplit cosy room with the chill wind whistling about the windows outside, it seemed already made for her.

'I don't really want to go back tonight, Mark. I would love to stay—only . . .'

'Only you're scared someone at the office might find out? Well, they might have to some time, my dear, but there's no reason why they should know exactly what you do with your weekends. It's certainly not anything I should worry too much about if I were you. We'll be back to-morrow or early Monday morning, at the latest, and they need be none the wiser.'

'Then I'll stay, if you'd really like me to.' It didn't seem such a momentous decision after all and she smiled tremulously as he sat down again casually and resumed drinking his tea. If Sara imagined she felt a sudden slight tension in him she told herself quickly she was mistaken.

She felt at once incredibly lighthearted, loving him more because he was so considerate. Not only did he wish to spare her a rough journey, he also seemed concerned that she should enjoy the weekend. She laughed across at him happily, her blue eyes dancing with even a trace of recklessness. 'I don't know if you planned this, Mark Fenwick, but if it was just a spur-of-the-moment idea what do we do for dinner? A boiled egg would do for me, but I doubt if it would satisfy you!'

He glanced at her and grinned as he stretched his long legs to the heat. 'It must have been at the back of my mind. I did dare hope,' he admitted. 'I did a lightning swoop on a large London store before we left this morning. Most of it I packed in the fridge while you were indulging yourself shamelessly in my bath, but you'll find a super casserole already heating in the oven. My housekeeper, in an emergency, has bought it, so I can almost guarantee its quality. Should you have refused to stay I was going to suggest eating it before we left. Sawing wood always did give me an appetite.'

They finished off the rest of their tea in companionable silence. That he didn't attempt to touch her made her feel confident she had done the right thing, and the remainder of the weekend stretched before her like a wonderful, impossible dream. Wonderful because she was going to have Mark for hours to herself. Impossible because never in her wildest dreams had she ever imagined anything like this happening. One day, she mused, she would tell him how she felt. Now it seemed enough to have him half asleep beside her in his chair, allowing her to dream a little herself.

Later, with an exaggerated yawn, he bestirred himself, suggesting pointedly that she might go and peer at the casserole and pop on some vegetables while he went upstairs and found a respectable pair of pants. When he did come down, bathed and changed and looking, with his thick hair brushed crisply about his head, disturbingly handsome, they ate at the kitchen table before carrying their coffee back to the lounge.

There was a record player which he switched on but

turned very low so that the music came only faintly from the background. After pouring liqueurs he put off all the lights except one so they might relax as they listened.

It seemed such a long time since Sara had spent such an evening and she knew a violent longing for a home of her own again. The stormy, isolated bleakness outside, the warm glowing fire within—and Mark! Mark, especially, turned this desire into a kind of fever.

As if sensing a little of her unspoken torment he didn't move to a chair of his own this time, but drew her gently down on to the settee and kept his arm around her. After a while he pulled her closer to his side as the sensuous music washed over them, but it was much later before he did anything more than hold her lightly. When eventually he did it was as if he acted idly, without really thinking, and Sara was only half aware of the arm around her tightening or that he determinedly turned her towards him so he might drop a brief kiss on her lips.

It was only a comforting caress to begin with and she felt nothing but a drowsy, pleasurable sense of contentment. His head lifted almost immediately, one of his long fingers tracing the clear-cut lines of her face before slipping beguilingly over the vulnerable hollows of her throat.

'Do you like being here with me?' he asked softly, his lips moving indulgently against her small ear, his arm hard and firm around the softness of her body.

'Yes, I do,' she whispered, nodding her head so that the silky dark curls touched his cheek, not able to keep the knowledge from him or to resent his asking.

'You'll be telling me next you're glad we met?' he murmured, his fingers wandering even further, finding the deep cleft between her slight, girlish breasts.

'Yes,' she was having some difficulty with her breathing, the tremors which were running through her affecting her voice. 'At least I could never regret it.'

'Nor I.'

She smiled faintly, moving her smooth forehead a little

against the roughness of his chin. She didn't realise then that gentleness might cloak his real objective. The sensuous movement of his fingers was so captivating there was no room left for fear. 'Mark,' she almost sighed his name.

'You didn't care much for me at first, did you?'

With a hint of seriousness she replied, 'I was actually very scared of you, but I don't think you stopped to consider whether you liked me or not. A little nonentity, I believe you called me.'

'I don't believe it!' he frowned in mock despair, kissing her softly again, implying by the insistent pressure of his mouth that she must have imagined any dislike on his part. When she scarcely dared respond he pressed his finger firmly on her bottom lip, prising it open. 'That's better,' he murmured as his mouth came down again, teaching her deliberately how to kiss him properly, so that her body relaxed and curved compliantly to his and her hands stole with barely disguised longing about his broad shoulders.

When at last he moved away she knew a small shiver of resentment and almost followed an urge to move towards him in his corner of the settee. Afterwards she realised this was how he had intended she should feel, that he must have laughed at her for a naïve little fool. A fool, but a fully experienced one! This was the bit which hurt.

As she stared at him, her heart in her eyes, he turned his dark head lazily. 'I think you should go to bed, Sara. All the fresh air this afternoon must have made you tired, to say nothing of the hard work.'

'I'm not very tired,' she mumbled, feeling strangely more alive than she could ever remember and curiously reluctant to leave him. These moments were to be treasured, they might never come again. She wouldn't mind staying here for ever, if only Mark felt the same. When his arms left her she felt an awful coldness and wished they were still around her. However, there was tomorrow. Perhaps she was being silly, in too much of a hurry? Before they left for London he might discover he liked her as much as she liked him.

'If you say so, Mark,' she said quickly, when he made no answer to her last remark. She decided dejectedly that he must have had enough of her for one day.

'You'll find the bedroom nice and warm.' He made no attempt to disguise a smoulder of satisfaction at the back of his eyes as he rose, drawing her smoothly up beside him. He dropped another brief kiss on her lips as she raised a transparent face to his, her mouth responsive.

Her smile was sweet as she met his enigmatical glance. 'Goodnight, Mark. I don't like depriving you of your bed, though. Can't I help you to——'

'No, run along,' he cut in, obviously requiring no assistence with blankets. 'You won't deprive me of anything—I'll see to that.' He paused, then as if feeling there was no need to elaborate, gave her a gentle push doorwards.

It seemed unbelievable, afterwards, that not a thread of suspicion had crossed her mind. Maybe because she had been so drugged with his experienced kisses she was reduced to a state of dreamy distraction, her common sense deserting her. And going upstairs nothing immediately happened to jerk her back to harsh reality.

She tried to hurry as she used the bathroom, thinking Mark might only give her so much time if he wanted to shower. Swiftly she brushed her small white teeth with the brush she had begged, then rinsed her face, glad there was no make-up to cream off. There was no cleansing lotion, but her clear, silky skin would survive very well on soap and water. She hadn't a nightgown either, nor had Mark suggested anything about this. It had occurred to her that she might ask him for a pyjama jacket, but she hadn't wanted to embarrass him. Or was it, she wondered breathlessly, that she hadn't wanted to embarrass herself, as bed and pyjama jackets might give an alarming sense of intimacy when Mark and she were here on their own. She could always sleep in her undies.

Scurrying back to the bedroom, she switched off the main light after slipping out of her dress and laying it carefully over a chair. The room, as Mark had promised, was lovely and warm, now that the electric heater had had time to take effect, and moonlight came softly in through the still undrawn curtains. Padding happily over to the window on bare feet, Sara stood gazing out on to a silent world, wrapped deep in the white magic of snow. It traced the green branches of trees, glazing the ground like fine white icing, glinting where the frost and moonlight caught it. It was beautiful but made Sara realise that outside it must be extremely cold, and she felt grateful for the warmth around her, the bed covered with its huge continental quilt that promised snug dreams.

How long she stood there entranced, her eyes lingering on the snow, her thoughts half on Mark, she wasn't sure. A faint noise, no more than a creak, of the door startled her and she swung around only to find herself bumping into the very man she had been thinking of so insistently. He must have entered the room quite silently, with the stealth of a big cat.

'Sara.'

'Oh, Mark!' for a moment she was too relieved to heed the deepening tone of his voice, 'what a fright you gave me!'

'Did I?' If his question contained a faint note of disbelief she didn't notice. He didn't stop a little distance away as she vaguely expected, but came right up to her, his arms reaching out to enclose her. 'I thought,' he said huskily, 'you'd be in bed.'

'I—no,' her voice faltered weakly as she tried to beat down a panicky conviction that this was wrong. Wouldn't she simply make herself seem stupid if she jumped too hastily to the wrong conclusions? If she managed this badly she might not only do this but might also destroy the new and still delicate relationship between them. He had, more than likely, just come to see if she was all right. He mustn't know she felt faintly apprehensive.

Yet she couldn't prevent herself stiffening a little when instead of letting her go he tightened his arms around her. Her eyes widening, she gasped, 'I was admiring the snow before getting into bed. We don't see much of it in Town.'

Disregarding her restraint, his hands slid up her slender back to pull her closer, his eyes mocking her as his breath lightly touched her bare shoulder. His voice came low in her ear. 'You can forget about London, Sara, for at least a couple of nights, maybe longer.'

'I know—but . . .'

'No more protests, my darling.' His hand lifted to curve her soft chin, tilted her parted, trembling lips towards his swiftly lowered mouth, so she was unable to avoid him.

His mouth was firm yet soft, implacable but yielding too, and Sara found her arms, instead of pushing him away, going around his broad shoulders. His embrace was suddenly tighter, holding her close and hard, his mouth no longer tender but fierce and demanding. Shamefully Sara became aware she had no real desire to escape him. He appeared to be wearing nothing but a towelling robe which gaped open and she felt her own compulsive reaction as he crushed her against his bare chest and one of her hands caught on his hair-roughened skin. The passion in him, which he had previously held in check, he allowed full rein, and Sara was conscious of a matching feeling rising tumultuously inside her.

'You're beautiful!' his mouth eased to whisper gentle, reassuring endearments against hers as he quickly slid the straps of her slip over the sloping curve of her shoulders so that it fell, a slither of silk, to the floor. As he stared down at her near-nakedness in the dim moonlight she saw his eyes smoulder with renewed desire.

'Mark . . .' She scarcely knew where she found the breath to protest, not with such a flood of passion running so dangerously between them. It was consuming her like a sweeping tide, but suddenly she seemed to see it as something she must accept. There must be a first time for everyone, and if Mark loved her as she loved him it would be all right.

Swiftly he was undoing her lacy bra with hands which betrayed some experience in such matters, and she could feel a feverish heat running through her beneath the probing, ruthless movement of his fingers. 'Mark,' she breathed faintly, unable to stop her awakening body drifting bonelessly towards him, 'do you love me?'

She didn't notice his slight hesitation as his mouth moved across her taut breasts. 'You're very sweet,' he muttered thickly, 'very easy to make love to, but do we have to talk now? It's too late.'

Closing his mouth deliberately over hers cut off coherent thought and she made do with his brief reply. His caresses on her bare skin became an ecstasy to make her cry out, and, as his kisses deepened, she felt the hot response of her own senses. A kind of primitive mindlessness took over, forcing her to cling to him dizzily. Dimly there moved through her swimming head the conviction that if Mark loved her such feelings could never be wrong. It might be indiscreet, but wasn't it the modern thing to do? No one thought anything of it any more and surely no harm could come of it. As she felt his hands on her breasts, hips and thighs, the wave of desire that appeared to be consuming him flooded Sara also. She made no struggle but merely tightened her own grip when he lifted her with a low, inarticulate exclamation and carried her to the bed.

She felt his weight settle beside her as he leant half over her as she lay submissively on the dark quilt, her soft body white and yielding. This time when his arms went around her she wasn't able to control the low moan which escaped her as his hands continued their intimate exploration. His mouth trailed points of fire over her bare skin until she could do nothing but press herself against him hungrily, and when his lips found hers again, damply, she wasn't conscious of anything but the hard pounding of his heart

over her own, the hard length of his powerful limbs forcing
hers apart.

Suddenly she was aware he was speaking against her
burning mouth. 'Do you care what happens tonight, darling,
or can you look after yourself? I don't want to have to do it
for you. Right now I don't know if I could. I've never
wanted anyone so much in my life.'

Look after yourself? Shock immediately stormed through
her as she slowly realised what he meant. The answer had
to be no! Every inch of her body which he had aroused to
such responsiveness cried out against it, but there was no
way she could honestly avoid the truth. He imagined she
was an experienced woman, while she didn't know a thing
about it. Yet while warning bells rang in her passion
drugged head she couldn't think absolutely clearly. It was
as if she floated on a fiery cloud, not completely conscious.
There seemed no way she could hold back the truth.
'Mark,' she faltered, finding it difficult to speak at all, 'I've
never made love with a man like this before, so I don't think
I know how to. I mean . . .'

As her voice faded, leaving her sentence unfinished, she
felt his instant withdrawal—if not immediately with his
body, in every other way. It was like a chill wind she didn't
understand. His hand left her breast as his mouth lifted
completely from her softly quivering lips and she heard him
swear half under his breath before he said harshly, 'You
mean this would be your first time.'

'Yes.'

'My God!' Suddenly, with a disgusted groan, he rolled
away from her and before she quite realised what was happening he was off the bed, apparently indifferent in his
quick fury as to what she might see in the moonlight. As
it was the hard strength of his masculine figure barely
registered through her painful bewilderment.

'Mark!' she stared up at him blindly, her arms reaching
out desperately. 'Please, darling, don't leave me!' So badly
did she want him back beside her she felt no shame that she

could plead so. She could feel, with every sensitised nerve in her body, the change in him, sense the anger which had replaced passion, even though the exact cause evaded her.

'Sara!' he turned, bending to her again, obviously trying to control his temper. 'You are telling me the truth? You've never been to bed with a man? I don't have to spell it out!'

'No,' there was a faint but audible sob in her voice, as she met his hard eyes, 'but there has to be a first time. And if we love each other—intend getting married——'

'Love!' she shrank from his curt laughter. 'I doubt if either of us knows the true meaning of the word.'

'Mark!' Her clear young voice was shocked, dazed, entreating.

'Don't bother to offer yourself again, if this is what you're doing! Let me tell you, Sara, I've never taken advantage of an inexperienced girl yet, and I don't intend making you the exception.'

'But . . .'

'No buts, either! I may never have been personally involved with a virgin, but I've heard enough. Do you think I want to be responsible for the pain and tears, the endless recriminations? Not when I can walk out of here and find all the pleasure I want without any of these complications.'

'I . . .'

'Why did you agree to stay the weekend?' he asked savagely, not allowing her a word, eyeing her so contemptuously that she shrank against the very pillows where he had kissed her so hungrily only minutes ago.

'I didn't think,' she began, agonisingly.

'What a pity you didn't!' his voice taunted sarcastically. 'Don't tell me you thought I was suggesting a platonic weekend?'

'I . . .' Sheer misery weighted her voice, making it almost impossible for her to go on. Could she, with absolute truth, answer yes? 'I didn't think it would be like this, anyway,' she stumbled. 'I thought we would get to know each other better.'

A snort of disgust was all the reply she got to this and she saw his dark face was savage as he stood staring down at her. He seemed, in spite of his obvious anger, to be imprinting the sight of her, her tumbled hair, her slender, sensuous body in his mind. As if her innocence and young loveliness was tempting him to stay beyond everything. Sara was shocked and disconcerted by what he had said, but his face reflected his momentary thoughts so clearly something shameless responded unconsciously.

'Mark, please!' She held out thin young arms.

'God, you've all the makings of a proper little bitch, haven't you!'

His words hit her like a much-needed douche of cold water, so that instantly aghast, she struggled to find a sheet to cover herself.

'The proverbial Eve,' he sneered, 'looking for a fig-leaf. It makes me wonder!' Suddenly, with a brief exclamation, he laid a restraining hand on hers. 'You're sure you've never slept with a man?'

'No!' Tears stung her hot eyes at his snarling persistence. 'Nor would I now!'

It must have been too late in the day to reverse the attack. Her hand was flung away and before she could move again he was across the room, his voice coming back to her curtly. 'Goodnight, Sara. I'm going to leave you to dream alone—and don't imagine I ever loved you.'

The door closed with such emphasis behind him she could never doubt he meant every word! No amount of pleading, she sensed, would alter him. Not that she would be willing to try again, with shame such as she had never felt before coursing through her, but what he said aroused an almost physical pain, bringing another dry sob to her throat. Stunned, she stared at the closed door which appeared to waver strangely in the moonlight. He hadn't advised her to sleep well, for which she should probably be grateful. Maybe he had spared her that, guessing from her tormented face that she would sleep no better than he would.

Far from sleeping, Sara wept for the remainder of the night, sleeping only as tears repeatedly exhausted her, awakening when, in her dreams, Mark's hard mouth ruthlessly crushed her own, only to find her arms empty. Never had she imagined anything could hurt like this, but it was a heartache made worse because it sprang from several sources. There was Mark and his mocking, outright rejection of her. Her own stupidity in thinking he had grown to care. Then her greatest folly in offering what had obviously held little real appeal for him. It was a bitter pill to swallow that his feelings for her, whatever they might be, had been incited merely by the thought of a licentious weekend. If only, she wished hollowly, it had been like that with her!

Eventually she must have fallen into a deeper sleep of sheer exhaustion and it was after ten when she awoke. At first she couldn't believe it was true; until she saw the sun shining, she thought her watch must have stopped the night before. In fright she jumped out of bed, only to be forced to sit down on the edge of it again until her head stopped spinning. She felt awful and suspected she must look it.

The sick feeling going from her throat at last, she reached numbly for her brief underclothes, remembering unwillingly the expertise of Mark's fingers as he had dealt with fastenings and straps. She shivered, though the room was still warm, but it wasn't cold that sent a quiver knifing through her. It was the memory of Mark's arms, and the things he had said, his ultimate rejection. Yet maybe she should be feeling grateful? Perhaps his ruthless treatment of her could have saved her from massive regrets this morning. With a nervous hand she straightened her slip and brushed the heavy hair back from her heated brow. She must have been crazy to have acted as she did, and even more insane to have agreed to stay here with him, even though she loved him. All she wanted to do now was get back to London!

Sara dressed swiftly after that, not stopping to do more than rinse her face and teeth briefly in the bathroom, ignoring the bath which might have taken some of the ache from her limbs and eased the painful tension in her head. Her appearance didn't worry her at this stage so much as the immediate situation between herself and Mark. Even the thought of going downstairs bothered her terribly. There was no sound to indicate how he might be feeling, no cup of tea by her bedside to show he might consider forgiving her. How did a girl face a man after a fiasco like last night?

A quick, horrified glance in the mirror did nothing to bolster her confidence. The face reflected there was so dreadfully blotchy! She had never been able to weep without leaving abundant evidence of tears, which was perhaps because she didn't give way to self-pity very often. This morning she was dismayed, if not surprised, to find her eyes swollen and puffy, her mouth looking vulnerable and hurt. Bathing her eyes several times didn't seem to help much and at last she gave up. All she could hope was that Mark might never spare her a second glance, or indeed a first one!

Reluctantly she went downstairs after drying her hands. The silence of the cottage smote her afresh, giving her the odd feeling, before she reached the kitchen, that Mark wasn't there. To her relief he wasn't. The only sign of him was in the note which lay on the wide table. It stated abruptly the obvious—that he had gone out but would be back shortly after ten when he hoped she would be prepared to leave for London.

Shortly after ten? Hastily Sara checked with the clock. It was that now, and she wondered how long he had been gone. There was an empty cup on the draining board but no sign of any breakfast. If only she hadn't slept so late! It was a blessing, she supposed, that he hadn't come back and found her still sleeping. Not knowing what else to do she ran back upstairs and, after tidying the bed, pushed her few things into her suitcase, carrying it down to the kitchen again ready for their departure. At least, she decided bitterly, he couldn't accuse her of keeping him waiting!

Not able to find anything else to put straight and feeling that even a cup of tea might choke her, she wandered listlessly over to the door and looked out. The snow was still there but the sun shone from a clear blue frosty sky, promising a fine if cold day, just the sort of day for walking happily over fields, exploring woods before returning to a cosy fire and lazy tea in front of it. A half sob rose in her throat as this reminded her of the sitting room and she went to take a final peep. As soon as she opened the door she knew it had been a mistake to do so. The fire was out, the dead ash in the fireplace reflecting her hopes so clearly that she turned miserably away.

Back in the kitchen she did eventually make a cup of tea, but without much enthusiasm. It was something to do, something to stop her thinking. While in the fridge seeking milk she noticed the large piece of meat, the pile of fresh steak, and wondered dully what Mark intended doing with it. Surely he wouldn't take it back to town and present it to his housekeeper?

A few minutes later she was still standing gazing at it when he came in.

'Good morning, Sara,' he spoke in what she recognised as his most detached voice. 'I hope you got my message all right and that you don't mind leaving. It's a pleasant morning.'

'Yes,' she returned his greeting brightly, making a great effort to sound completely normal but finding it impossible to look at him immediately. If he could pretend nothing had happened then so could she. She must prove she had some pride left! 'I'm just wondering,' she continued casually, 'what you intend doing with all this.'

There was a moment's silence, as if he was slightly astonished by her cool tones. 'Leave it,' he replied curtly. 'I'll give it to the people I told you about, who look after the place. I can ring them from town. They have a key and will come and collect it and switch off the electricity.'

'Oh, I see.' Because it seemed to emphasise all the things she didn't know about him, Sara felt the rawness of despair touching her throat and she closed the fridge door unhappily. Listlessly she picked up her coat which she had placed conveniently over a nearby chair.

As she made to pass him, her head lowered so he couldn't look at her properly, he grasped her arm, halting her, his distant manner momentarily leaving him.

'No, you don't see, Sara,' he said coldly. 'It's not what I usually do as there's rarely need, but you wouldn't want me to advertise that I came prepared for a much longer weekend than we're actually having?'

'Mark, I——' scarcely realising what she was doing, Sara glanced helplessly from where his hand lay on her arm up into his terse face, allowing him to see hers for the first time.

She heard his indrawn breath rasp, but whether it was because of her ravaged face she had no idea. His jaw clamped hard on a bitten-off exclamation she couldn't decipher, but whatever it was he didn't attempt to repeat it. He merely gave a curt shrug, his indifference to her obvious suffering very apparent. He removed his hand from her arm.

'If you're not feeling so good this morning, Sara, it might console you to know I don't either. I'm not going to hold any inquest, if this is what's worrying you, but in future I'd advise you to make your position quite clear before you agree to spending another weekend with a man.'

Shrinking from his insulting tones, she muttered bleakly, 'So you've already said.'

He went on, his grip tightening cruelly at what he must have mistaken for impertinence, 'You let me say things no man should have uttered to a girl as innocent as you. Didn't you understand the danger? Some situations take a lot of pulling out of—more than you realise!'

'Mark!' her voice was strangled, her head lowered again

at his savage tones, as she recalled unwillingly how he had felt forced to leave her just as passion between them had mounted to a dangerous peak, 'I told you I'm sorry. I know I was wrong about the weekend, but I had the wrong impression.'

'You thought you'd be returning to London with a wealthy fiancé? For heaven's sake, Sara, don't stand there looking as if such a thing had never occurred to you! In my profession one becomes a past master at reading between the lines. You gambled and it didn't come off, but you can't really hold me responsible.'

CHAPTER SIX

SARA stared at Mark, feeling her blood run terribly cold. If she had thought of marriage it hadn't been until he was actually making love to her in the bedroom. Nothing had been planned, premeditated, as he sneeringly suggested! Suddenly anger stirred in her breast and she felt like slapping him. 'You're beastly,' she cried. 'I wouldn't have anything more to do with you even if you begged me! I hate you, do you hear, hate you!' Her choking breath would not allow her to go on, but her blue eyes darkened with the force of her feverish emotions as she glared at him.

She must have said enough as his mirthless laugh contained little amusement. It was merely a sarcastic twist of the lips. 'Get into the car,' was all the reply he made, and this coldly. 'I'll join you in a minute.'

All the way back to London Sara sat in frozen silence and Mark made no attempt to speak to her after assuring her that they should be there about one. She knew he was merely acquainting her of the time, that he wasn't issuing an invitation for lunch, and the afternoon stretched before her like a limitless, dreary void.

She realised it wouldn't be just this afternoon that she wouldn't be seeing him again, but couldn't yet assess how she would feel, not until the first numbness wore off. Having had no breakfast, along with everything else, was making her weak and tearful again and, in order not to make a fool of herself, she closed her aching, tired eyes. When she opened them it was to find Mark shaking her. They were in London, outside the hostel.

Dazed she blinked up at him, scarcely aware that she must have fallen asleep, her face very young and unguarded. At first she thought his hands strangely gentle and there was a look in his eyes she didn't understand as he watched her coming awake. If it was tenderness she saw there it must have been an illusion, as his expression hardened to one of indifference as she struggled upright.

'We've arrived.' He spoke in a completely detached voice, which mocked her fleeting impression that he could feel compassion as well as other things.

'Oh!' A wave of scarlet rushed to Sara's white cheeks. She had intended sitting coolly, with detached dignity, and had done neither of these things. Bemused, she gazed at the tall, disciplined man by her side, seeing herself minutely reflected in the chill grey of his eyes, eyes which were glittering strangely as they surveyed her closely. 'I'm sorry, I didn't realise.' She swivelled unsteadily, her hand groping for the door lever, not even aware that Mark made no attempt to assist her.

As she left the car and turned he deftly passed her case. 'I have to be away this coming week,' he said, 'but I expect I'll see you around some time.'

'Yes. Goodbye,' she breathed, an inaudible murmur as she clutched her suitcase clumsily to her shaking breast. She failed to see how his fingers whitened on the steering wheel, as if held there by determination, as she turned and left him.

The rest of the day, as did the following week, passed for Sara in a kind of dazed blankness. Never had she thought time could become so meaningless or that anything which wasn't entirely physical could hurt like a continual, excruciating pain. She tried desperately not to think of Mark and what had happened, but found this almost impossible.

At the office the girls teased, 'You look as though you've been crossed in love, young Sara!'

At once she felt like screaming, telling them to shut up and leave her alone, but all she managed was a rather sickly grin which convinced her tormentors they were nearer the mark than she was ready to admit.

'Isn't he going to see you again, then?' they taunted.

'No,' she confounded them by confessing frankly, 'he isn't. If you must know, it wasn't even serious and he's had to go away.'

She saw them losing interest, murmuring indifferently about there being other fish in the sea, and while it was better to have loved and lost he might, if she were patient, come back to her.

Sara smiled, trying to pretend she didn't care all that much but agreeing that he might. She could have told them he never would. Mark had made this abundantly clear. He wanted no more to do with her and was leaving her to extinguish her suffering as best she could. He had also made it quite plain that he considered her as much responsible for what had happened as himself. This haunted her, but not as much as the memory of his arms holding her close, of his passionate, ruthless kisses. She longed to be able to forget.

It was several days before she understood that if she continued to work at Astro's she could never hope to do this. Even if she didn't see him there was talk of him in the office all the time. That he was away at the moment didn't appear to stop it to any extent. Someone produced an old copy of a German newspaper, showing him with a gorgeous blonde, and Gwen had a cutting from heaven knows where in which he was photographed on his last trip to Venezuela, dining out with a dark-haired beauty. Both women, Sara reflected bitterly, looked much older—and wiser—than herself. At least they didn't appear to be simple young girls in whom Mark brutally denied any lasting interest! If she were to regain any peace of mind Sara knew she must leave here as soon as possible.

It was just after reaching this decision that she met Dicky Gordon again. She hadn't particularly wanted to see him, in fact she had hoped not to. Their friendship had so little going for it, it seemed pointless, but he was waiting one evening outside the hostel where she could scarcely avoid or ignore him.

'Hello!' he exclaimed, winding down the window of his

car as she approached. 'Care to have dinner, darling?'

She was used to his careless, slightly affected tones and they didn't influence her answer. 'Not really, Dicky,' she replied carefully.

'Oh, come on!' he used his favourite form of persuasion, grinning up at her like an appealing small boy.

'I'm sorry,' she said, then hesitated. On second thoughts what had she to lose? Mark wasn't here, and if he had been he wouldn't want anything to do with her. The empty hours of the evening stretched endlessly.

Cleverly, as Sara frowned down at him, Dicky gauged her uncertainty although she didn't realise it. 'You'd be doing us both a good turn, you know.'

Eventually she gave in, but when he picked her up an hour later she still wasn't sure why either of them bothered. They weren't even good friends, neither did they make any noticeable effort to be. Half the time while they were out together they didn't even try to talk to each other but sat idly contemplating their own thoughts. Usually Sara felt at ease with him, but it was only because he didn't seem to matter, and tonight anything must surely be better than sitting in the hostel thinking of Mark.

The evening differed little from that of others Dicky and she had shared. It was only after they had eaten a rather dreary meal that he suggested something more unusual. 'Why don't we go to my flat and play some records? I make very nice coffee, better than we get here. Quite frankly, Sara, I don't feel much like a film tonight, or anything else, for that matter.'

Because he sounded so depressed she agreed, if doubtfully. 'But only for an hour,' she warned. 'I don't make a habit of visiting men's flats, and I live in a hostel, in case you forget. They don't approve if we stay out late.'

'I'll remember,' he grinned. 'I'll also promise not to try and seduce you, my prim little Sara.'

This brought back the memory of her weekend with Mark too vividly and she flinched while her face paled.

'You'd better not,' she smiled, but her eyes were serious.

What happened later she could never have foreseen, not with the greatest foresight in the world, and the shock and subsequent repercussion was to stay with her for a long time.

Dicky's flat was in South Kensington and it was almost dark as they passed the junction of Brompton Road and Thurloe Place. She recognised, in the street lights, the high façade of the Victoria and Albert Museum where she had spent several hours one afternoon. In a way, she mused, she was going to miss London, if only because she had not yet had the chance of getting to know it properly. This part of London, she knew, was full of history and interesting places. Not far away, along Cromwell Road, there was the Natural History Museum, set back from the roar of traffic, among plane trees, and beyond the museum, up Queen's Gate, was an international residence for scouts, with a chunky statue of their founder, Lord Baden-Powell. This was only a short distance from Hyde Park Gate and a nearby quiet cul-de-sac where number 28 was the town house of Sir Winston Churchill.

Sara was so busy attempting to pick out and mark various points of interest, not the easiest thing to do at this time of night in a car, that she was surprised when Dicky drew up in a quiet corner. 'Here we are,' he said.

His flat surprised her, being much smarter than anything she had imagined. It was quite large and pleasant as well as being in a fairly select district. He must be much better off than was immediately apparent.

'It belonged to my parents,' he explained, seeing her slightly startled expression. 'The old man's dead, but he left it to me. My mother still uses it occasionally when she's home from Australia.'

Sara nodded, accepting his brief if not very explicit explanation without curiosity. At least it was feasible. His mother probably helped with the rates and whatnot, and Dicky must have a better position with Astro Chemicals than she had thought. Come to think of it, at a second glance, the whole place looked fairly shabby, so perhaps he wasn't so affluent after all.

As he promised, his coffee was good and his records, if not quite to Sara's taste, were bright and easy. She found herself relaxing for the first time that week, even consenting to dance once or twice when Dicky asked her. It was well after ten when she firmly rose to go and he drew her unexpectedly into his arms.

'Sara,' he whispered, 'you're so sweet. I'd like to kiss you.'

Knowing she should be pushing him away, Sara found herself suddenly wondering what it would be like to kiss someone other than Mark. Could she have imagined the way he made her feel? Might she not have exaggerated the ecstasy? Wasn't this a chance to find out? No harm could come of it as she was just about to leave and was sure she could manage Dicky.

'If you like,' she smiled at him lightly, even trying to joke a little. 'Just one for the road.'

She tried not to stiffen as his lips found hers, nor to think of other, harder ones. The kiss went on and on, Sara not realising how close and intensely he held her as she marvelled at the way she failed to feel a thing. Not even when she waited was there a flicker of emotion, nor did she find her body responding as it had done beneath Mark Fenwick's expertise.

Then suddenly she became aware that Dicky's lips had left hers and his arms were no longer around her. She heard his brief exclamation, a muttered curse, and for a moment she stood bewildered until a woman's high-pitched scream rent the air.

'Richard—how could you do this to me! How could you!'

Blankly Sara's eyes widened as she unconsciously clutched her head, thinking there was something wrong with her hearing. Then, as she swung around in a kind of horrified amazement, she found herself slowly freezing as she met the contempt in a pair of icy grey eyes. It was Mark!

'Oh no!' she thought, her almost audible moan of despair mingled with Dicky's far from silent expletive as she stared blindly from Mark to the weeping girl on his arm—a girl who had every appearance of being on the verge of hysterics. She noticed that even while Mark never removed his eyes from herself, his arm went around this other girl as if trying to protect her. As for Dicky, he stood, his face a dull red, looking extremely guilty, which might have annoyed Sara in any other circumstances as she didn't think he had anything to be feeling guilty about. It was Mark's bewildering presence which caused her own dismay.

Momentarily Sara closed her eyes, as if unable to believe the evidence in front of her, but when she opened them again he and the girl were still there. She saw the girl's tears turning rapidly to anger before her gaze went back to Mark. 'I thought you were still away,' she said helplessly.

Mark's cold glance met hers, slaying her on the spot. 'That can have nothing to do with this.' A sneer touched his lips as he dismissed her trite statement. Nor did he spare her a second look as he turned ruthlessly on Dicky. 'You apparently feel put out at our appearance, Richard, but I suggest you owe your wife, who also happens to be my sister, an explanation.'

'Your wife!' Shock moved visibly across Sara's face as she swung to Dicky.

'I told you about her,' he muttered truculently.

'Told me about her?' Sara repeated, knowing he lied. 'Of course you didn't!'

Mark cut in, his voice harsh as clearly he didn't believe her, 'I don't care what you told your girl-friend, Richard. It's my sister who has all my concern.'

'I don't know what you're getting so bothered about,' Dicky replied. 'Surely you of all people wouldn't begrudge a chap a bit of fun? Besides, Hilary and I have been washed up for some time.'

Mark looked as if it would have given him great pleasure to have knocked Dicky to the ground, but Hilary said sharply, 'You can have your divorce, Richard. I won't fight it any more, if it's what you really want.'

Sara found herself gazing at her in a kind of cold horror, as the nightmare seemed to deepen. She had had no idea Mark had a sister, nor Dicky a wife. Hilary was older than she had first thought. She must be around Dicky's age, her tinted blonde hair and round brown eyes made her appear younger, but Sara saw now this was only an illusion. Nevertheless she was very smart, expensively dressed and attractive. What more could Dicky want in a wife? Above all, how could he have taken another girl out, pretending he was single?

She heard her own voice breaking in as Hilary went on wildly about a divorce and Mark seemed unable to quieten her. 'But Dicky doesn't want to marry me, Mrs Gordon.'

Hilary's hand went up as if she would have liked to strike Sara. 'I don't care if he wants to marry you or just continue to go to bed with you! That's your look-out! All I want is a divorce!'

'Hilary——' Mark gripped his sister firmly by the arm, his face pale as Sara swayed dizzily and was forced to grasp the back of a chair to steady herself. 'I don't think any satisfactory purpose can be served by remaining here. We'd better go. You can talk this thing out with Richard in the morning. I'll see Miss Shaw personally, myself, at the office. I promise you she'll be sorry.'

'I might have known she worked in the same place!'

'Mrs Gordon!' Making a great effort to pull herself together, Sara tried again, even while she trembled at the open condemnation on Mark's face as he stared at her. 'I'm sorry this has happened, but you've got it all wrong. Dicky and I are just friends, scarcely that, in fact.'

'You're wasting your breath, Sara.' Dicky's cool interjection could be taken different ways and didn't help much. Sara couldn't look at him—she was finding it increasingly

difficult to look at any of them. The room was beginning
to spin with the combined weight of their awful derision.
Mark's was worst of all; it seemed to be crushing her, tearing her apart, there was nothing but the most terrible pain!

'Come along, Miss Shaw.' Mark was suddenly at her side,
grasping her ruthlessly, his voice so deliberate that Sara
found herself wondering if there could ever be a situation
where he didn't take complete control. 'I'll drop you off. I
think you've done enough damage here. It might be wiser
to give Richard time to pull himself together, to decide
what he really wants, and whom!'

'Mark, you'll let me come with you to your place, please?'
Hilary pleaded, turning her elegant back on a sullen
Richard, as if she really didn't care what he decided or if
she never saw him again.

'Of course you can stay,' Mark assured her, 'for tonight,
anyway. But we must take Miss Shaw with us, you understand.'

He picked up Sara's wrap from the settee, almost flinging
it at her, his face totally grim as he turned to guide Hilary
through the door. Without another word or glance at a now
completely silent Dicky, Sara followed.

The next day the sun was shining when she went along to
Mark's office. Fortunately he had instructed her when to
come the evening before so no one knew about it, as, she
realised, must have been his intention. Almost she had
decided not to return to work so as to avoid seeing Mark at
all, but pride forbade her seeking this way out. She had
little doubt he would ask her to leave the company immediately, but if she could face him for the last time with
her chin up, it might be some consolation in the future.
The future Sara tried not to think about, moving as it did
so bleakly before her.

As she approached Mark's domain her face was white,
though no more so than it had been all morning. She had
rubbed a little blusher into her cheeks which she suspected

made her look worse. Even Miss Gregg had been concerned, to the extent of advising her to take the day off, but Sara had refused. Soon, she might have told Miss Gregg, she might have every day off, but the words somehow stuck in her tight throat.

She went straight up to the top floor, glad that Miss Drew would be out. She didn't think she could stand any more sympathy, no matter how kindly meant, and what Miss Gregg saw, Miss Drew would undoubtedly see too! She didn't wait in the outer office but knocked at Mark's door and went right in.

He was there, on the telephone, conducting a conversation he didn't interrupt other than to wave her curtly to a chair.

Reluctantly Sara sat down, recalling that it was the same chair that had inadvertently begun her strange friendship with Mark all those weeks ago.

She saw him cover the mouthpiece quickly with his hand before speaking to her harshly. 'I expect you know what this is about, but before I throw you out there are several things I want to say. If you'll just wait a moment.'

It was an order, no polite request, and she felt her limbs trembling terribly, forcing her to do as he asked whether she wanted to or not. Even to walk the length of the room would have been too much, under his glittering gaze.

She nodded numbly, trying not to look at him, but found her eyes wandering towards him hungrily, clinging, in spite of herself, to every beloved line of his face. There was a fearful, growing conviction in her breast that this would be the last time. It had really been over between Mark and herself last week. Fate, in bringing them together again, had merely been bestowing a particularly cruel bonus. She might even look on this interview as a few more straws to clutch, but that wouldn't make it any better.

With an unsteady hand she caught the ends of her tumbled hair, pushing it back with a nervous, convulsive movement, unable to meet any longer the smouldering look of anger in his eyes as they rested on her. If he so obviously hated her, why should she break her heart? Men, she decided bitterly, were much the same, whoever they were. There was Mark and his harsh attitude down at his cottage. Then Dicky, and his equally unfair treatment of her. That Dicky had a wife was something which still amazed her! Didn't a man feel obliged to tell a girl he was married any more? Apparently not. Of the two perhaps Dicky's attitude was the most confusing, as she didn't think for a moment that he loved her or had been looking for the kind of relationship his wife obviously suspected they shared. As for his wife threatening to divorce him—Sara almost gasped with renewed horror. Surely she couldn't be serious, or if she was surely Hilary didn't intend to involve her? Somehow she must make Mark understand she was innocent of anything that might hurt his sister. If he wasn't prepared to believe anything else, he must believe that!

'Well, Miss Shaw?'

Sara was suddenly aware he had put down the receiver and was staring at her, still with the utmost dislike in his eyes. She started, her hands leaving her hair, clutching her fingers tightly so he wouldn't see how they trembled. 'Mark —Mr Fenwick, I realise you're furious.'

'Furious,' he interrupted grimly, 'is not the right word. Disgusted might be more accurate.' His glance searched her ashen face. 'It should be some consolation to know my sense of perception wasn't wrong, you really are a little tramp! Only I was too slow to take advantage of it.'

'How do you mean?' Sara's head throbbed so badly she couldn't work it out for herself. She could merely stare at him with pain dulled eyes.

'At the cottage!' he all but spat out. 'Pretending you were but a simple young virgin who'd scarcely known a man's arms. More fool me!'

She flinched as if he had struck her. 'You didn't want me either way,' she flung back at him, tormented beyond sensibility by his contempt.

His mouth twisted in an ugly sneer. 'I considered myself well rid of you—little dreaming I wasn't. Last night, in White's flat, I realised the depth of your scheming!'

'Whose flat?'

'Whose flat!' Mark repeated derisively, controlling himself with obvious effort. 'Richard White's flat, of course. My brother-in-law. Who the hell do you think I'm talking about? Don't tell me you embrace men before you even know their name?'

'Richard White!' Sara breathed, Mark's insults going over her head. 'But I've always known him as Richard Gordon. Once, soon after I joined Astro, I got lost and he stopped to see if he could help me. He introduced himself as Richard Gordon but insisted I called him Dicky. I certainly didn't know he was Richard White.'

Mark halted sharply, a frown drawing his brows together darkly. 'You mean you had no idea that Gordon was his second christian name? That his surname is White? You've never heard of it?'

'No, at least . . .' Sara gazed at him, her own brow pleating in some bewilderment. She had heard the name once or twice in the office but had never connected it with anyone she knew. 'I seem to remember the girls mentioning a Mrs White, but I wasn't even aware you had a sister. If I had and known she was married to Dicky do you think I would have gone out with him?'

Indifferently Mark shrugged. 'Names make little difference. This could simply be a well thought out story. Don't forget I heard Richard declaring he'd told you of his marriage.'

The hint of colour returning to Sara's cheeks slowly faded as she looked despairingly down at her hands. There was a depth of hopelessness in her voice. 'I don't know why he said that. It wasn't the truth.'

'What proof have I that you are speaking it?' he sneered.

'I'm not lying.' Her voice sank to a whisper at the bitterness which crossed his face.

'You can try telling that to the judge! You won't mind the publicity of a divorce case?'

'Oh, no!' Panic surged in Sara so strongly it brought her gasping to her feet. 'Mark,' she cried wildly, her blue eyes anguished, 'you must believe me! I don't care if you never see me again, but I swear I did nothing with Dicky that could give your sister any reason to seek a divorce.'

'You were at his flat—in his arms,' he retorted viciously.

'It was the first time—for both,' she faltered miserably. 'We very rarely saw each other. He asked me to go out with him last night. I—I suppose he caught me at a vulnerable moment, when I was remembering you. I couldn't stop thinking of the way in which I'd annoyed you,' she lowered her head. This sounded better than mentioning her heartache. 'He was outside the hostel and it seemed an opportunity to—to cheer myself up. I hadn't been in his flat an hour, and then I only went because he seemed down somehow. I felt sorry for him.'

'Sorry for him!' Mark's tight fist rested on his desk as if he restrained baser impulses. 'Let me tell you that young man's had more help than enough, and most of his troubles have arisen from his own stupidity. I think you might well transfer your misplaced sympathy to my sister.'

'I did apologise. I said I'm sorry.' Sara swallowed, fighting desperately to keep back tears. Mark's hardness horrified her. It seemed something she couldn't reason with, especially when he looked at her with such hate in his eyes.

'Words, Miss Shaw,' he continued, 'can rarely undo the damage of something that has already taken place. I arrive back late from an impossible conference to find my sister having hysterics in my drawing room over a husband to whom she has only been married half a dozen years. Don't you think I've enough to do without having to sort out the matrimonial tangles of my relations, to say nothing of the morals of a loose little typist?'

'I'm telling you I didn't know!' Tears were streaming

down Sara's cheeks now, but she didn't care. Standing there, so near to Mark and yet so distant, she felt she would never care about anyone or anything again. If it hadn't been for her aunt and uncle, the memory of her dear parents, she would have turned and run. For their sakes she didn't want her name trailed through the mud, and not when she'd done nothing to deserve it.

'Please, Mr Fenwick,' she entreated, a sob disturbing her voice, 'you must prevent this divorce. How did your sister know I was at his flat, anyway?'

'Don't worry,' he sneered, 'I didn't tell her. She came down unexpectedly from their house in the country and went straight to the flat. Actually she had an appointment early this morning which she'd overlooked. She had tried ringing Richard earlier but couldn't get any reply. When she arrived at the flat she heard the record player and a woman's voice and naturally came for me.'

'I see.'

'She was extremely upset.'

'I'm sorry.' Sara took a deep breath, trying this time to stem her tears. Tonelessly she said, 'How tired you must be of weeping women.'

'I am.'

Sara's pulse thudded dully as he rose to his feet and came around to where she stood. She stared up at him, her eyes bewildered, like those of a child. 'What are you going to do?' she asked.

His mouth tightened as her voice broke. 'You can return to Coventry, Miss Shaw, and I'll do what I can. Though why I should bother is beyond me, but if you want to repay me don't ever let me see you again, here or anywhere.'

'You'll never believe I'm innocent?'

The taunting curl of his lips told her before he spoke. 'I told you before what I believe. There's a name for girls like you.'

Suddenly, before she could control it, Sara's hand flew out and caught the side of his mocking face, the slap quite audible in the quiet office. 'Oh, God!' Her fingers went horrified to her white lips.

A second later she was in his arms, her hand torn aside as his mouth crushed down brutally on hers. It could only have been a few seconds but was enough to make her reel on her feet with shock when he let her go.

There was blood on her lips and she was shaking. Even Mark must have thought he had gone too far, as when he freed her the utter paleness of her face seemed to keep his eyes riveted on her for a long, tense moment. Sara was scarcely conscious of his intent regard as she struggled to control the dizziness which threatened to overtake her.

She heard Mark say tersely, as if he could take no more, and didn't intend to, 'You appear to attract trouble, Sara. I'll get a man to run you straight back to your hostel. I'll do all I can for Hilary and Richard, but I want you out of London, otherwise I promise you'll suffer.'

'I don't want your help, Mark.'

'Maybe not,' he had the last word, which he threw at her grimly, 'but you'd better be prepared to accept it!'

That was the last time she had seen him in almost three years. Occasionally she had caught glimpses of him in newspapers which lay around the hotel, but such photographs she deliberately ignored, wishing only to forget. Or at least get over the heartache she continued to feel whenever she thought of him.

Two weeks after leaving London she had received a brief note assuring her that she wouldn't be cited in any divorce case, but there had been nothing after that. It was as if an erasure had been drawn over the few months she had spent there and they had never been. She had told her aunt and uncle that London hadn't suited her, that she had been homesick and wanted to come home—small lies which she hadn't been proud of telling, but what else could she have done? She had felt even more ashamed when they made such a fuss of her, declaring that they could see for themselves that she should never have left. Aunt Loretta even wept a few tears which had made Sara feel even worse, especially when she found it impossible to confess the truth—that she had fallen desperately in love with a man who didn't want her and had almost been the cause of his sister's divorce!

But she never forgot how good Loretta and René had been to her during those first awful weeks. They helped her get a job, not protesting over-much when she declined to work full time in the hotel. She had started with the moderately sized chemical firm of George Dent—the brief but explicit reference which Mark had enclosed with his note having helped her here. In this she had been more successful than she had dared hope, partly, though she didn't clearly see it, because she dedicated herself almost entirely to her new job, wanting nothing else but to lose herself in work. She could never recall working so long or so hard, or of earning so much praise which she felt guiltily she might not deserve.

For a long time after returning from London she had dared hope a miracle might happen. Her heart had been sore, but with youthful optimism she had eventually allowed herself to hope Mark might come to miss her. When she remembered the kisses they had exchanged at the cottage she was convinced he must care for her a little, in spite of his harsh words, yet he never came. She grew weary of looking for a letter, a telephone message that never arrived. Of sitting in the foyer of the hotel, her eyes fixed on the revolving doors, seeing all the wrong men walking through them. On the day when she finally accepted that he wasn't coming she had just wanted to die. As she couldn't do this she decided she must forget him completely and, during the months which followed, while she didn't actively grieve for him so much, in some peculiar way her emotions became frozen. She never went out with other men. She had no desire to and refused to go merely because they seemed to find her attractive and asked her.

It was only at weddings, Christmas parties and such which she felt duty bound to attend that she ever danced or had much to do with men socially.

Naturally her whole attitude in this respect bewildered and puzzled her aunt and uncle, who were forever pointing out the wonderful advantages of matrimony. René, particularly, being half French, had moments when he lamented loudly that his beautiful niece was wasting the best years of her life and marriage was what every sensible girl needed. 'You should look for the right man,' he would declare, 'then you'll be happy ever after!'

They were too busy to dwell on the subject, however, for which Sara was grateful. Sometimes, though, she found herself thinking wistfully of a husband and children of her own, but how could she marry when Mark Fenwick's tall figure still came between her and every man she met?

Now, after almost three years, when she was nearly twenty-three, it seemed she was to meet him again, and she had no means of accurately assessing her own reactions. If at first she had been stunned, almost terrified, she began to realise it could be the best thing that had ever happened. Hadn't she read of similar situations many times in the novels which she perused on those evenings when she wasn't helping in the hotel? People very often found that after not seeing someone for years they no longer even liked them, and the advantages of proving they didn't far outweighed any continuing, cowardly desire to avoid them.

Wasn't she tired of going through life feeling only half a person? It wasn't as if she looked very different. She had lost her last remnants of puppy-fat and developed in the right places, but underneath she must be different. Climbing swiftly out of a now cold bath, she shivered, praying it was so. Otherwise, she grasped the thick, fleecy towel almost fiercely, heaven help her!

A month later Mark Fenwick arrived. George, who hadn't felt well the day before, declared he would be relieved when it was all over. He said, too, that he was glad Mark wasn't a man who was keen to be shown all the ropes. 'He likes to form his own impressions and work on them, from, of course, the fundamental data.'

George, however, was there to welcome the new boss on his first morning. 'He would like me around this week,' he told Sara. 'After that I can stay at home. I feel rather like a boy given permission to leave school!'

Sara tried to smile, recognising a little of Mark's cool, well known authority.

George went on, 'Do you know, Sara, I'm actually looking forward to it.'

Sara supposed she should be happy for George. Happy he should feel this way about what was for many men too big a hurdle. It was nice to see someone looking forward to retirement. She wondered if she would feel the same, thousands of office days hence. She tried not to think of herself, she had been endeavouring not to do so for the last four weeks and had striven to lose herself in work. Consequently she had lost weight and her eyes were shadowed, but otherwise she looked her usual efficient self.

Broodingly in the mirror Sara considered herself—smart, intelligent, even sophisticated with her hair grown slightly longer and for neatness pinned smoothly behind her ears. Did she really want to be like this? Where was the impulsive, passionate girl she used to be? Would Mark prefer her as she was now, or would he remember the warm-hearted, younger version he had held in his arms at the cottage?

Sara sighed, recognising by the rather excited expressions on several faces she passed as she left the cloakroom that Mark must already be here. She lingered outside. With all the makings of a first-class coward she contrived to put off meeting him as long as possible. She even bent, pretending to adjust the buckle of her strapped shoe which was perfectly all right as it was. He might not have come. He could have sent someone else. The offices here were large, by any standard, but could never match the huge glass and stainless steel palace in London where Mark reigned supreme. She couldn't understand why he should want to come here at all, unless it was a challenge. He would never be able to resist that!

It was while she was meditating and fiddling needlessly with her shoes that the door of George's office opened and she heard his voice.

'Ah, Miss Shaw, you've arrived!' His throat cleared, fussily. 'Mr Fenwick, I should like you to meet my—I mean your new secretary, Miss Shaw. I think you will find her invaluable, as I've already pointed out.'

So in the end there was no way Sara could avoid the meeting she had dreaded for weeks. Her fingers visibly trembled as she straightened and her face went fearfully pale as she met the full impact of Mark Fenwick's enigmatical eyes.

CHAPTER SEVEN

AFTERWARDS, Sara decided glumly she might have been doing something that proclaimed her state of mind less obviously than fiddling with her shoes! When she first became aware that Mark was actually standing looking down on her, she felt for a second as normally foolish as any girl might have done caught in such a position by someone of his importance. Then suddenly, amazingly, all feeling inside her seemed to disappear, to be replaced, as she met his inscrutable gaze, by a delightful if surprising numbness. It was so real that she felt sure if anyone had stuck a pin in her she wouldn't have felt it, and, without attempting to analyse it, she felt very grateful. No matter what happened next she would always appreciate how she had managed this first and surely the most important meeting with such commendable poise.

She even found herself whispering a small prayer of thankfulness under her breath as she straightened and smiled at him, unconsciously fingering the belt of her blue dress. Blue had always been her lucky colour. Whether it was or not it certainly seemed to be helping her this morning. This and the talisman she wore around her neck and the four-leaved clover she had found last week and popped into her pocket. And—Sara stopped, frowning sharply, realising how ridiculous this would all sound if related. More foolish still when she considered how she hadn't needed any of these lucky charms after all. At the last minute she had been protected against Mark Fenwick by her own indifference. As her wide eyes reluctantly met his she felt not one inward quiver.

Never having been able to so much as glance at him before with even a fraction of such equanimity, she im-

mediately concluded that she had completely recovered
from her brief infatuation. Mark's eyes were strangely almost as blank as her own and he held out his hand politely
as George made his stumbling introductions. When George
asked if he recalled meeting Sara, he indicated briefly that
he did.

'You were with Astro Chemicals in London, Miss Shaw,'
he said soberly.

Sara's gaze wandered, like a sleepwalker's, from the calculating grey of his eyes to their lightly clasped hands, 'Yes,'
she replied, tugging her hand free.

He released it at once. 'You weren't with us long?'

'A few months.' As if he didn't know! A hint of sharp
indignation swept through her, but her new-found coolness
held. 'I scarcely thought you would remember me?'

George broke in before Mark could reply, 'Men in our
position, Sara, never forget a face.'

Wryly Sara wondered how George could expect anyone
to remember individually the hundreds of employees at
Astro's, but perhaps it was better he should think so. Congratulating herself that no betraying colour reached her
cheeks, she merely smiled. She was calm, and remained
this way, when she had expected to feel as devastated as a
delicate forest exposed to the heat and ferocity of a tropical
storm!

Mark said very little more, but he did continue to regard
her rather closely. Probably wondering, she thought bitterly, why he should be burdened with the girl who had
wrecked his sister's marriage. Perhaps already he was debat-
ing how to get rid of her, or even how he might punish
her further. That it was only revenge he meant to deal out,
Sara had no doubt. If he had had any feeling for her at all,
other than that of dislike, wouldn't he have contacted her
long ago? It was no use deluding herself that he cared for
her in any way, but somehow this no longer seemed to
matter. She must be mistaken about the gleam of satisfaction in his eyes as they momentarily held hers. If she wasn't

she couldn't imagine why it was there, as the few questions he went on to ask were all connected with her work. Not one of them was remotely personal.

For the remainder of the day Mark was cloistered with George in the main office and out touring the works. At five-thirty, while they were still out meeting some of the personnel, Sara decided to go home. If it had been anyone but Mark she might not have gone without waiting to see if there was anything else she could do. As it was she considered she had done enough for one day, and George had said to leave when she was ready.

While still relieved that she hadn't felt shattered at meeting Mark again, this evening she wasn't quite so confident. Her head ached, and through her whole body she was aware of a curious, bewildering weakness. It was rather like delayed shock, although, as the thought occurred, she quickly dismissed it. Mark could have no power to affect her adversely now, not when she didn't care for him any more.

Unfortunately such conclusions didn't stop her from thinking of him on and off for the rest of the night. He hadn't changed much, he didn't really look that much older. The lines about his mouth were deeper, but his hair was still as thick and dark, his eyes as keen as ever. It was no use trying to fool herself that hearts wouldn't begin to beat as fast here as they had done in London. He still had that distinctive masculine quality that would soon have the other girls swooning, but, she thought sarcastically, he would know how to deal with them himself! He was staying with George for the next few nights in George's country house just outside the city. George had said the actual take-over was taking longer than he had expected, but it was comforting to know George was going to be here as a kind of buffer until she got used to having Mark around.

During the next week or so Sara managed both to keep her distance and prove her worth. She didn't know why it should become important not to get too near Mark, but it was for her pride's sake that she strove to convince him of her intelligence. In London she had merely been a junior typist and had never worked with him before. Now she was an extremely good secretary and she told herself repeatedly every morning that this mattered more than anything else. She still retained, however, her former resolution to leave as soon as possible.

Near the end of the second week, just as she was returning from one of the other departments, the door of the main office opened and Mark stood there.

'Oh!' she exclaimed, unaccountably flustered at the way he was looking at her. 'Do you require anything more, Mr Fenwick? I was just about to go home. Perhaps Mr Dent——?'

'I take it you've been out somewhere, otherwise you would know George has gone,' he interrupted.

'Oh,' Sara bit her lip, 'I see. You must intend going yourself, then? The weather seems to have worsened. It's not a very pleasant evening.'

This time she was startled to notice his jaw go really tight. While congratulating herself on her serenity she was conscious that she felt extremely wary. It might be wise not to antagonise him too obviously.

'I'm going to be quite a while yet,' he replied, his even tones giving no clue as to whether he was vexed or pleased about this. 'I would like a word with you before you go, though. Now that we don't have the admirable George standing between us like an over-protective father.'

He turned and she followed in rather shaken bewilderment. Weakly she heard herself protesting, 'I'm sure that's not his intention. We can't have anything to discuss that he couldn't hear.'

'Of course not,' Mark's voice was deceptively smooth. 'There's nothing I wish to say that I would object to George hearing at all. It's simply the opportunity to say it which mysteriously appears to be escaping me!'

'I'm sorry.' She was forced to sit on the chair he pulled out as she couldn't think of an excuse not to do so. She blinked uncertainly when he chose to seat himself opposite rather than behind his desk, where she might have felt safer. In some peculiar way she realised she was suddenly bursting to say quite a lot herself. Not that she could understand him sharing the same inclinations as he had made no attempt to contact her over the last three years. Now the opportunity had arisen, she knew a feverish urge to confront him angrily, but could sort nothing constructive from her confused thoughts. Fervently she wished Mark had never sought her out like this. It might only be about work, of course. Hopefully she glanced at him, but unable to sustain his unexpectedly close scrutiny she looked away again apprehensively.

Her fingers curling tightly, she waited, in the rather fraught silence, for him to speak. His opening sentence didn't worry her unduly, although it startled.

'For a moment,' he said enigmatically, 'I thought every trace of the old Sara was gone, until I saw the nervous flutter of your lashes. I recognise this more easily than I do the depressingly hostile façade you've presented since I came.'

Something warned Sara just to sit tight, that if she remained unruffled everything would be all right. Proudly she tilted her rounded chin. This helped, even if she couldn't quite meet his taunting gaze. 'I haven't meant to be unfriendly, sir, if this is what you mean. I've learnt a lot in three years'—let him make what he liked of that!—'and I've worked hard to prove I can be a good secretary. Mr Dent thinks I've succeeded admirably. He wants me to convince you, but I expect this will take time.'

'How many times,' Mark jeered, 'have you rehearsed that insane little speech? Have you any idea how you sound?'

'Really, sir . . .'

'God, Sara!' Anger flashing in his grey eyes, he rose to his feet again. 'Can't we have something a little less formal? I feel I'm talking to a machine!'

Shivering, she tried not to look at his taut, hard face.

'That's what I like to think I am, during office hours,' she retorted stubbornly.

'And what about out of them?'

'I—well, you needn't concern yourself any more with my private life, sir!'

The emphasis she placed on her last word would, she hoped, defeat him, but he came back instantly, his brows pulling darkly together, 'I asked you a question, Miss Shaw. I'll decide myself what I concern myself about.'

'And if I'm not prepared to answer?' she exclaimed.

'Then I should simply take it you have something to hide.'

Some of her coolness deserting her for a second, she said quickly, 'I can't think why you should be interested in what I do in my spare time.'

'It depends what you mean by interested, Miss Shaw.' The little coolness she lost seemed to attach itself to him. 'I could merely be showing a polite, if unappreciated, regard for my new secretary. How do you imagine we're to work together if you continue to be so antagonistic? Surely,' his voice softened persuasively as his eyes caught and held hers, 'surely we can talk to each other properly, Sara? Dispense with ill feeling after all this time?'

What he meant by that exactly she wasn't sure. In her uncertainty she eyed him cautiously, a fragile young creature, disposed to shy nervously at the first wrong gesture. She wasn't sure what he was talking about, but she did know she had no intention of getting hurt again. 'I don't think we were ever sincere friends, Mr Fenwick, if you must rake up the past, and, as regards my job, I would like to leave as soon as possible. I know,' she rushed on before he could speak, 'I told Mr Dent I would stay, but I've given it considerable thought since. I'm thinking of applying for a post abroad. It seems foolish to stay in the one place all my life.'

'I see.' He stared at her narrowly and his broad shoulders shrugged as he examined her tense face. 'Just so long as you're sure what it is you really want. If you give me suitable notice I'll take steps to replace you. I can do this quite easily,' he added, while she swallowed in sudden dismay and a hint of temper, 'but I would be grateful if you would stay a few more weeks, until I get properly settled in. Was there any particular part of the world you wanted to see?'

'I—yes,' Sara floundered, not wholly prepared for such a question and feeling her cheeks go scarlet, 'America, maybe. New York.'

'I see. On your own?'

'Of course.' Her confidence returning at the thought of such beautiful distant places, Sara smiled.

'So this means there's no one you'd be reluctant to leave behind. A fiancé, perhaps?'

'Not yet,' her smile faded stiffly as she became aware of the trap he so neatly set. 'A girl can have fun, though, without becoming seriously involved.'

'You enjoy having fun?' he had the air of a man who was having it at her expense.

Sara said resentfully, if not all that truthfully, 'Yes.'

His mouth curled. 'Exactly how would you describe this fun you have, Miss Shaw?'

'Really, Mr Fenwick,' she rose quickly to stand beside him, retaining her coolness with difficulty, 'I'm sure my comparatively uninteresting social activities can't interest you. You must have much more exciting ones of your own. If that's all, sir, I really think I should be going.'

'Sure,' he was staring at her and suddenly he shrugged carelessly. 'You appear to be parked on a kind of island, Miss Shaw, and your isolation seems remarkably complete. Or maybe I'm the only one who can't find his way there?'

'Goodnight, sir.' She didn't stop to work out whether this was an insult or not. Mark had always been enigmatical! It wasn't until she reached her bus stop that she realised she was shaking.

All the way back to the hotel she felt odd, yet somehow she didn't—or wouldn't—connect it with Mark. Why had he called her into his office? she wondered. Perhaps she should have waited to find out and not left so hastily, but while she had been there, he had certainly not asked the kind of questions she had been expecting. In fact, if she hadn't known better, she might have said the conversation had moved a little beyond what he had envisaged, and her reactions, in some way, hadn't altogether pleased him. Certainly he had made no attempt to detain her longer as she had almost raced through the door.

Men, she fretted, as she mounted her bus and it lurched on its way, were too egotistical. Mark probably didn't realise she didn't care for him any more. Had he expected her to stand before him quivering with the love he had once so firmly rejected? Perhaps she should have made it quite clear that any feeling she had had for him had definitely died. But if she had still loved him she would certainly never have told him. Had he expected he would be allowed the pleasure of laughing at her again? Sara's hand tightened painfully on the back of the seat she clung to and she didn't see or hear the man who rose with interested appreciation to offer it to her. Nor did she notice that he sat down again with an impatient, if rueful sigh.

At the hotel Sara took the lift to the top floor, going swiftly along to her own small room to change. She had promised to do an hour on reception as one of the staff wouldn't be in until later. Her room wasn't large but had its own private bath and over the last years she had added various personal touches which gave it an air of homely comfort. Swiftly she scrambled into another dress, not waiting to have a shower, silently cursing Mark for detaining her so long as she brushed her hair before rushing back to the lift. Uncle René and Aunt Loretta were both in London and she didn't want to let them down, especially while they were away.

It was just as she reached the desk that Mark walked in. He not only walked in but was followed by one of the porters carrying two large suitcases. If he was as startled to see Sara as she was him, she didn't know. She was too busy contending with her own consternation to wonder about the size of his.

He came straight over to reception and she was glad she had the width of the foyer in which to compose herself. Halting beside her, he didn't pretend not to see her but stared right at her.

'Might I ask,' he drawled suavely, 'if you actually work here, or have I got the wrong impression?'

'No. That is,' she corrected hastily, 'I do help out occasionally for my room.' Which was nothing short of the truth.

'I see,' he was as formal as if he talked to a near stranger. 'Well, Miss Shaw, if you are here to serve and doing nothing, you can look after me. I'm sure this should please you! I booked a room, a suite to be precise, and I should like to be shown to it as quickly as possible.'

Sara took a deep breath, her eyes widening as she hastily groped for the record book which contained the bookings. Yes, here he was. Swiftly she checked. Mr Mark Fenwick, there could be no mistake. He had booked a suite on the second floor, one of the best they had. Surely it couldn't be so? She must see someone!

'Miss Shaw,' his eyes glinted, 'you've proved, these last few days, that when you choose you can work quickly. You can't expect me to stand here all evening.'

He didn't bother to lower his voice and the head receptionist came over, more than a little interested by Sara's obvious confusion. Charmingly she took charge of the situation. 'Number thirty-eight, sir. We've been expecting you.' She passed the keys to the waiting porter and while Mark signed the register she politely proffered, 'Jennings will take you up. If there's anything at all you require, sir, just ring. We have an excellent room service.'

'Thank you,' Mark replied, rewarding her with a charming smile, while Sara stood frozen.

'I must say, Sara, you're not being very bright.' The girl

sighed in audible appreciation as they watched Mark's tall figure disappear into the lift. 'It's not often we have some-one quite like him. I shouldn't mind doing his room service myself!'

'Oh, shut up, Betty!' Sara felt like screaming, panic rising inside her, not admiration. 'I'm sorry,' she apologised, at Betty's offended face, 'I don't know what's got into me.'

'You'd better find out, honey,' Betty laughed unkindly, 'otherwise I might believe it had something to do with our new guest?'

'Don't be such an ass!' Sara managed a creditable smile as she stood wondering what on earth she'd do now. Mark obviously had every intention of staying, and she had acted like someone in a trance, making no protest. Hysteria, like nothing she had ever known before, rose in her throat. She didn't want him here, where she would be falling over him at every corner! If he stayed here, it fol-lowed, he might discover everything about her—that, among other things, she had no intention of going abroad or anything else! Worse than this, he might destroy her new-found peace of mind. She had a horrible suspicion —she had had it since her interview this afternoon in his office—that he might do this again very easily.

It puzzled her how he had arrived at this particular hotel. She didn't think George would have told him as he had advised her that it might be better not to let Mark know she did extra work in the evenings. Nor could Mark have known it belonged to her uncle as in London he had never enquired or seemed inclined to talk about her relations. Be-sides, in the hotel, her uncle was always referred to as Monsieur René, as it was good publicity. At least it had been when he had first started, and the habit had seemed to cling. People seemed to think the hotel must be extra good if there was a French connection and, after all, Uncle René was half French. No, Mark must just have chosen at random—but, before he ruined everything, she must get rid of him!

Somehow, dazedly, she got through the hour, then turned to Betty. 'I'm off now as I see Doreen has just come in. She should be with you in a minute.'

The Criterion, with its thick carpets and luxurious furnishings, wasn't the type of hotel where people hurried unduly. Consequently a few elegant eyebrows rose at the sight of an attractive young lady almost running along the second floor corridor. They might have been even more surprised to have seen how the same young lady conducted herself during the next few minutes!

The Oyster Suite, so named to suggest something slightly beyond the ordinary pocket, was situated a little distance from the lift. Still without stopping to consider properly what she was doing, Sara positively thundered on the door.

The slightly ominous silence that followed tried her beyond endurance after the first few seconds. Without waiting for an invitation she wrenched the rather old-fashioned knob her uncle retained and burst in.

Mark was standing in the sitting room, a glass in his hand. He had removed his jacket and was staring at the door, a narrow frown on his face as if curious to know who clamoured so presumptuously to gain entry.

'Why couldn't you answer?' she shouted at him, trembling.

The only indication he gave that he considered her behaviour out of the ordinary lay in the faint and familiar tightening of his lips. He did say, however, 'Is this the usual way you treat your guests at the Criterion? Is it customary for a receptionist to invade a man's bedroom and shout at him into the bargain?'

This went over Sara's head like so much water. Maybe he did have something to complain about, but she had never felt so worked up about anything in her life. She certainly had never lost control before, not to the extent of acting in such a rash manner. Hastily, as a small note of warning sounded in her head, she tried to be calmer. 'It's not exactly your bedroom, Mark, and if I appear a little distraught perhaps I've good reason to be. You can't possibly stay here, and I shouldn't have to come and tell you so.'

'Oh, can't I?' His eyes glinted a little at her renewed use of his name, otherwise he gave no indication of how he felt, either about her statement or her obvious agitation.

'No!' She closed the door behind her before stumbling towards him, gazing up at him with fear-darkened eyes. Unconsciously her voice sank to a hoarse whisper. 'You know you can't, Mark. You're my boss!'

His hard laughter was totally disbelieving as his glance went over her flushed, passionate face. 'Not good enough, Sara, I'm afraid!' He placed his empty glass on a table but didn't refill it, nor did he offer her anything. 'You'd better try again.'

Confused, she drew a funny little breath, changing her tactics, silently apprehensive that she hadn't stopped to think this properly out before confronting him.

'How did you know I was here, Mark?'

'I didn't.'

'You didn't?'

He looked vaguely impatient. 'Do you have to repeat everything, Sara? I seem to recall it's a habit of yours. If you must know I did faintly remember you giving me this address to write to when you left London, and I decided, if the hotel was still here, it would do as well as any other as a place to stay for a few months.'

'A few months!' Her heart almost stopped.

'There you go again!' His teeth glinted white, though there wasn't too much amusement.

Sara merely reiterated, parrot fashion, 'A few months?'

'No longer,' he held her startled, too brilliant gaze. 'Much shorter, I assure you, if I accomplish what I came for sooner.'

It could have been some consolation to know he might soon be gone—if she hadn't felt so terrible! Everything inside her seemed to be melting, she couldn't seem to find her former, gratifying calmness, though she strove to hang on to the last remnants of it. Turning from him, she fought for some kind of composure. 'I know what you felt about me when I left London.'

'Did you, Sara?'

'You didn't exactly make any secret of it,' she choked bitterly. 'Don't you see how impossible this situation could become, and it's not as if there aren't other good hotels in the city. How can I stay here, work here properly, knowing there's no respite from your hate!'

His dark brows rose. 'Don't you think you exaggerate everything out of all proportion, Sara? I don't think I've ever managed to hate you for longer than five minutes at a time. You certainly aroused some strong emotions, but very rarely that.'

When she merely shrugged angrily he laid a firm hand on her shoulder, turned her around again. 'I dislike talking to someone's back, especially yours.'

She felt his hand on her shoulder like a brand and her voice shook. 'You know I'm not making mountains out of molehills!' Her face whiter and more haunted than she knew, she stared up at him. 'I was responsible for causing your sister a lot of unhappiness and I realise you can't ever forgive me. I read about her divorce on the grounds of incompatibility. I suppose you saved me from being involved, but I know you must blame me.'

'What a lot of conclusions you've arrived at,' he jeered. 'True, she and Richard were divorced, but they've both remarried and seem wonderfully content with their new partners. My sister is living abroad and I rarely see her. Believe me, you can stop worrying.'

'It still doesn't alter the basic facts,' she cried. 'I suppose,' she went on wildly, 'you might have married yourself since I left London?'

'Not yet,' he drawled, mildly, 'but I hope to. And very soon. In fact I don't know how I'm bringing myself to wait.'

'Oh!' This was all she could get out; she couldn't go on.

So there was someone? She might have guessed. For a moment, as her eyes closed against the pain of it, she felt herself trembling. It was like falling into a great void of darkness, shot through with shock. And because she had no way of coping with it she lashed out at him, 'All the more reason why you shouldn't stay here!'

His hands simply tightened on her shoulders as if he enjoyed the quiver going through them. 'If I could understand even one of your reasons, Sara, I might consider doing as you ask, but until you choose to give me a plausible one, I'm afraid I stay put. Why not? My rooms are exceedingly comfortable.'

As his hands dropped and he turned away, Sara caught his arm, suddenly alive with angry frustration. Hadn't he subjected her to enough pain in the past without exposing her to the same risk again? He must never be allowed to guess how she felt but, if only because he had misjudged her in the past, he must be made to understand he owed her something. She hung on to the arm which went peculiarly rigid beneath her tight clasp. 'Mr Fenwick, you can't! I won't let you. I——'

Whatever else she had been going to say was cut off abruptly as he pulled her close against him. 'Little fool,' he rebuked her, 'are you quite finished?'

As she tried to speak but couldn't he continued, his eyes smouldering on her averted cheek, 'You just listen to me for a change, Sara Shaw. I've had enough of your Mr Fenwicks and Sirs to last me a lifetime and I don't think you're quite so impervious as you'd like me to believe. If it's going to make you feel any better I'm willing to go along with it so far, but I've yet to be convinced you've forgotten all you felt in my arms. You were never averse to my kisses—and I'm just waiting to hear you call me a liar!'

Sara's heart stopped, then raced as anger played over his face and his arms tightened painfully. Every muscle in his hard body seemed to make contact with her own, bringing a response she seemed helpless to prevent. She knew he expected her to deny everything he said and, after she had done so, would deal out what he considered suitable punishment. Stubbornly, as she was too apprehensive to say anything, she remained silent.

One of his hands touched her cheek, exerting pressure until she looked at him. 'I know you couldn't forget so quickly, Sara.'

'Not so quickly!' Indignation, fighting with the liquid fire in her veins, loosened her tongue almost recklessly. 'It's been three years! And why should I remember anything about you when one of the last things you called me was a little tramp!'

'That hurt?'

'No,' she stared at him, conscious of his hand slipping to her neck as his thumb played lightly with her chin. She wanted to go on defying him but dared not, 'Yes,' she admitted, under his threatening gaze. 'Well, why shouldn't it, especially when I don't think I deserved it. I wasn't old enough ...'

'But you are now,' he cut in adamantly, 'older and quite able, it seems, to fight me on my own ground. I'm warning you, though, that if this is what you want, it won't be so easy for you this time. I'm prepared to make few concessions.'

'You never did!'

'You think not?' Suddenly, before she could guess his intentions, his hand snaked to her nape, grasping a handful of silky hair, pulling her head back. As she opened her lips to protest his mouth came down violently on hers, drawing a shattering response. Immediately and alarmingly her whole being seemed to fuse with his and she trembled at the surge of remembered feeling that rushed through her. A shock wave, as if their bodies, at least, were well aware of the attraction their minds chose to ignore. To Sara's dismay she found herself responding, her own treacherous passion betraying her. When he released her abruptly she was aware that her mouth shook. She also remembered, in one soul-shattering moment, that he now belonged to someone else.

It was his turn to be silent, not a muscle in his dark face seemed to move as his eyes lingered on her bruised mouth. Passion smouldered but was as swiftly subdued. 'Moments like this,' he said coolly, glancing swiftly at his watch, 'can save hours of argument and achieve much the same purpose.' His mouth quirked mockingly. 'I should like to stay longer, but I'm afraid I have a dinner engagement, one I wouldn't care to miss. So if you'll excuse me, Miss Shaw . . .'

If the first round seemed to be his, her turn would come! For the whole duration of a restless night, Sara found herself vowing it again and again. The next morning she had dark shadows under her blue eyes and her mouth had a wounded, vulnerable look she hadn't seen for three years, one she had hoped not to see again. Quickly she reached for a bright scarlet lipstick which, applied liberally, certainly detracted from the young hurt impression, but she wasn't sure she liked the rather siren effect any better. She regretted there wasn't time to rub it off and start again as she was late already.

In the staff dining room, which she liked to use when her aunt and uncle were away, she was just snatching a cup of tea when Betty came in.

'Good morning, Sara!' she exclaimed, so dramatically Sara wondered what was coming. She hadn't long to wait. Betty rushed on excitedly, 'You should have seen the woman our new guest took in to dinner last night. Quite took my breath away!'

As Betty was usually too worldly to be impressed by anything much, this information startled. 'New guest? You mean——?'

'The handsome Mr Fenwick. But you should have seen the glamour-puss he was with. She has—what do you call it—oomph, and some!' Betty paused, rotating her slinky body, snapping her fingers. 'South American, I would say. Doreen has heard there's one over here for the opening of that new show at the Belgrade next week, only she can't recall the name.'

It was a smooth morning at the office. It was, Sara realised bleakly, getting smoother every day. She had an uneasy suspicion that Mark could run this whole show with his eyes closed and was wasted here. The reason why he was here at all was becoming painfully clear, at least part of it. This South American girl must be the same dark-eyed beauty the press had caught him with in Venezuela. Sara wished feverishly that she had begged the cutting from Gwen as she could not remember the girl's name, only that she had been an actress or singer of some kind. She would probably be here for several weeks before opening in London and Mark must have decided to make the most of the opportunity. The taking over of George's business must be providing an ideal excuse to get to know the girl better without being hounded by newspaper photographers. It would also provide a reason not to commit himself until he was ready. He must be crazy about her, though, to have arranged to be here when she arrived. It convinced Sara more than ever that his kisses last night had merely been a form of angry frustration.

George went early and near four o'clock Mark rang for her. He had been on the line to London practically all afternoon and it had been her rather irksome task to keep all other callers at bay. When she entered his office in reply to his summons he looked faintly impatient.

'You'd think they could manage without me for five minutes,' he grated, the terseness not notably leaving his eyes as they rested on Sara. 'Come in, Sara, don't you dither, for God's sake!'

After the incident in his suite, Sara had scarcely been able to look him straight in the face all day. Not without her heart shaking as she remembered the strength of his arms. His kisses, though brutal, still haunted her, and she had always thought such thoughts were nocturnal, like owls, chiefly confined to the night. It appeared she was wrong.

Otherwise how could she explain a deep longing to be held close to him again? She advanced into the room, asking primly, 'I wonder why you didn't send someone else to take over, sir, as you so clearly can't be done without in London.'

'Sara!' his voice was clipped. 'If you say sir once more I won't be responsible. I won't warn you again.'

'I'm sorry,' she mumbled, looking at the floor, as if intrigued by the way the sun moved over the lino. She noticed he didn't answer her question and, thinking he dismissed it as more impertinence, didn't dare repeat it.

He gazed at her long and narrowly and she appeared to have no option but to stand while he studied her. His eyes went all over her, from the top of her silky head, down her long, beautiful legs to her small, arched feet, a procedure which should have aroused indignation but only succeeded in reminding Sara poignantly of another time in the bedroom of a cottage. Fear that he might, simply by staring at her, discover how he still affected her forced her to return his glance indifferently. Never, she resolved, would she give him another chance to hurt her again, as he had done in the past.

At last, when she was wondering how much longer she could stand it, he spoke. 'Since last night,' he said, 'I've had little time to consider anything, as you must know, but I'm rather doubtful as to the wisdom of you having two jobs. How do you imagine you can work day and night, Sara, and continue to satisfy me?'

CHAPTER EIGHT

In the office one might have heard a pin drop. Sara had been expecting anything but this or she might have had an answer ready. She did find one quickly, even under the disconcerting concentration of Mark's grey eyes, but the atmosphere between them wasn't really conductive to pointing out that she considered it her own business what she did in her free time. It might probably be better to pretend to be confused, then he might not press the issue. 'I'm afraid I don't understand,' she said meekly.

He wasn't deceived. She had hoped he might be, but he wasn't. If anything he looked more forbidding than ever. 'I don't think I need to spell it out for you, Sara, but if you insist on being deliberately obtuse I will. This job and the one you're doing at the hotel. Surely it would be possible to find a room, a flat perhaps, without involving yourself like this? I can see how they must consider you useful with your secretarial training and ability to speak other languages, but I'm warning you I won't always find it convenient.'

How did he mean? Sara glanced at him beneath her thick lashes, rather like a child trying to weigh up a stronger adversary. He would jolly well have to learn that there were others to be considered besides himself! 'It works out very well, or it has done until now. I've always managed everything Mr Dent required of me. I have plenty of energy.'

'Which I want for my own use,' Mark returned cryptically. 'There's also a lot to do here. Astro's are international, but Dent's is quite a large firm and needs to be amalgamated carefully. It provides the kind of challenge that can profit a man in several ways, but he must have the right team, one absolutely to be relied on. In a situation like this

I consider my secretary to be of the utmost importance. Any energy you have left over I don't want you expending on further work at night.'

Sara retorted a little desperately, 'I assure you I've always coped very well in the past!'

'But George's pace is not, I think, mine.' Mark's eyes were keen on her dismayed face. 'Why have you found it necessary to keep so busy, Sara? Usually one only works like a slave in order not to think—or remember. I happen to know, from personal experience.'

She flushed, her cheeks going hot, then extremely pale as a quiver shook her. Fearing she looked guilty, she lowered her head. Maybe she was, but she didn't have to confess, nor would she allow him to wheedle it out of her! She said primly, still keeping her soft young face averted, 'I have my reasons, but I'd rather not discuss them.'

'So I must find out by other methods, if I'm granted patience!' His eyes smouldered suddenly. 'No doubt you will acquaint me of your decision in good time?'

His sarcasm was beyond her. 'You want me to choose between yourself and the Criterion?'

'If you like.'

'And if I don't like?'

'Then I might have to find someone to replace you.'

Sara forgot that only a short while ago she had requested him to do just that. Now it seemed to be a battle of strength with much more at stake than a mere job, though she wasn't sure what. Hastily she gulped, 'If you're worried that I intend barging into your suite at the Criterion then I can assure you I won't. I promise wild horses wouldn't drag me there again. I can't promise you won't see me around the hotel, but I'll do my best to keep out of your way and I won't even look when you're entertaining guests. And——'

'Please!' He held up his hand and she almost cringed on realising what she had just said. If he did notice, and she was sure he did, he gave no indication. 'All the promises and assurances in the world wouldn't make me change my mind,

Sara, but I'll be generous. If I haven't proved within the next two or three weeks that your extra job is impracticable you can continue it.'

Although she would have liked to argue, his expression prevented her. It didn't seem possible that her courage should fail her at the last moment, but it did. She could only manage a very grudging, 'That seems fair.'

'A better concession than you deserve,' he replied dryly.

Which didn't make it seem so fair after all! 'Plenty of people do two jobs,' she began insisting.

'Sara!' his piercing tone should have warned her. 'Get the hell out of here before I change my mind!'

Blindly, more than a little wounded, she turned too quickly and her foot twisted and shot out below her on the slippery lino. Unable to save herself, she fell, catching her head with an audible thump against the side of his desk. There she slumped, lying against it, counting the stars.

'Sara!' This time his voice was thick with alarm, unless the ringing in Sara's ears distorted it. She lay on the floor a minute longer, quite satisfied not to get up, a dark void beckoning so enticingly that she sought to lose herself in it. She felt herself lifted very gently against a strong arm, and a hand strangely soothing brushed back her hair, but it was the words being uttered under someone's breath on which she strove to concentrate, tried to hear but somehow could not.

When she could pretend to be unconscious no longer she opened her eyes. Mark still bent over her and her head hurt, but she didn't think it was too bad, not after the first shock wore off. Mark's face was so near her own and so obviously anxious that her heart lurched. 'I think,' she tried to smile up at him, 'that was a silly thing to do.'

'Just so long as you realise,' he retorted lightly, but he didn't smile and his eyes were grim. 'One shock after another. Can any system stand it?'

Who was he talking about? It couldn't be himself. She tried to guess if it was by a hazy examination of his features

but, as they betrayed nothing more, she had to give up. 'I'm
sorry,' she whispered. 'It was the lino.'

'I know very well what was responsible,' he said enigmatically, so dryly she felt she must have been mistaken
about his former concern. 'If you can manage to sit up, Sara,
I'll get the nurse to look at you before I send you home.'

'Oh, but it's only four o'clock and Nurse Brady will be
busy. Besides . . .'

'Don't argue!' He lifted her to a chair and there was a
certain terse appraisal in his gaze as he parted her hair and
examined her head properly. 'Only a small bump, but it
could have been worse. Brady will probably do no more
than look at it, but I insist she does this.'

Minutes later he had contacted the nurse and poured
Sara a liberal measure of brandy. 'Get this down,' he
threatened, 'even if it chokes you. You've caused me enough
bother for one day.'

A half an hour later Sara closed the door of her room
behind her and almost collapsed on to the bed. She felt
more shaken than she had liked to admit, although she
doubted it was altogether from the bump on her head.
Nurse Brady, though sympathetic, had assured her this
didn't amount to much and that, apart from perhaps a slight
headache, she should be quite all right by morning. Nurse
Brady had seemed more interested in Mark and had agreed
with him that Sara would be better at home, where he had
immediately dispatched her in his own car. He would, he
had said, have taken her himself if he hadn't had a meeting
with the shop stewards at four-thirty.

Sara sent a message to her cousin, who was in charge
while his parents were away, that she wasn't feeling too
good and could she be excused duties that evening? Claude
sent word back that it was quite all right and not to worry.
He would send Sara a light meal later on and see that she
wasn't disturbed.

Sighing with relief, Sara dragged off her coat and dress
and stretched full length on her bed. The sedative Nurse

Brady had given her had its effect and she dozed on and off until after seven when a waiter arrived with a tray. Surprisingly, as she went to take it from him, she felt much better. Her head still ached slightly, as Nurse Brady had predicted, but a little hot soup and coffee almost completed the cure. Afterwards she had a warm bath and instead of dressing again put on a loose peignoir over a thin nightdress, deciding to sit for half an hour before going back to bed. If she went too early she knew she would only toss and turn, thinking of Mark and the disturbing conversation they had just had.

Sitting in a chair didn't help much as her thoughts kept drifting towards him. Some, like puffs of summer cloud, she managed to disperse before they got too near. Others persisted, loomed blacker, threatening to envelop her. Why didn't he want her to do extra work here? Perhaps he didn't want her to see him entertaining his girl-friends of an evening? He didn't know the hotel belonged to her relations and maybe she should have told him, now that he was staying. Restlessly Sara stirred. It wasn't easy to know exactly what course to take with a man like Mark. One moment he looked at her as if he was still more than a little interested, the next as if she were a stranger who he was determined would remain so. Or at best, a rather foolish young girl who only added to his daily irritations.

So confused did she become that when a knock came she was glad of the diversion. Thinking it was the maid for her tray, Sara picked it up and carried it to the door. Even a brief word with someone might stop her thinking. To her surprise and consternation she found it was Mark, not a maid, on her doorstep.

Startled, she stared at him. He was the last person she wanted to see, even though she thought of him exclusively. How on earth had he found his way here? The staff would never dare tell him. 'How did you know where to find me?' she gulped, clutching the tray as if her life depended on it.

Before she could protest he had taken it from her, set it

down outside where it could be conveniently collected and turned her back into the room. Firmly he closed the door.

'A little bird told me,' he said mysteriously.

'A little bird!' Sara spluttered, her pulse hammering. 'I'm afraid I don't believe in them.'

'Well, you can always begin,' he rejoined grimly, 'but whether you do or not that's all the information you're getting.'

Numbly she shook her head, still dazed by what was happening, and colour flooded her cheeks as his eyes went over her thinly clad figure. 'You still haven't said why you're here,' she breathed.

'That should be obvious.' His steady gaze was fixed on her upturned face and his eyes held hers for several throbbing moments, moments when everything seemed lost, even the passage of time which seemed to stretch to eternity between them. How handsome he was—her throat seemed to contract as her eyes clung to his face, aware of how each separate feature enhanced his good looks.

She found herself overwhelmed by a sense of desolation, a poignancy of feeling that swamped her former resolution not to allow Mark any access to her heart again. Her resolve cracked and shook. How was she to keep him out? Yet to become involved as she had been before was surely to be avoided at all cost! 'I suppose you felt obliged to come and see me,' she said flatly, forcing herself to look away, 'but there was no need. I'm quite recovered.'

'Perhaps you are, but I'm not,' he muttered darkly. 'It was for my own peace of mind, not yours.'

What did she make of that? 'It was kind of you to let me go early,' she replied politely.

He inclined his head. 'Now that I'm here aren't you going to ask me to sit down? You could try being kind to me for a change.'

Her voice faltered. 'I might be willing, but a girl's bedroom is surely not the place.'

'It was mine last time—or don't you remember?'

How dared he evoke memories over three years old! The colour fled from her face. It was throwing the gauntlet and no mistake, but what could he hope to gain by it? His eyes, wandering down her figure, brought back vivid recollections of that night which she had always yearned so hopelessly to forget. She shook her head as words momentarily eluded her, clutching her flimsy wrap tighter around her quivering body. Why couldn't he just say goodnight and leave? Did he have to deliberately provoke her into recalling things she would rather not?

'I have only two chairs, as you can see,' she muttered evasively at last. 'I don't usually entertain men here.'

'I wasn't thinking of ringing for drinks and soft music,' he quipped with gentle irony, 'nor do I want to stay all night —this time.'

'You didn't ever,' she was goaded to reply, stung to bitterness. 'Not with me, anyway.'

'Be quiet, Sara!' His fingers bit as he guided her to a chair before taking the one beside it. 'You don't know what I wanted and you were too young to take on the responsibility of deciding what you wanted yourself. That is as you were then. Are you any older now, I wonder?'

'Twenty-two,' she missed his point as she groped to pull herself together. The thrust into her chair had disarranged her wrap and she strove futilely beneath his keen gaze to gather it around her again. 'Of course,' she breathed crossly, 'I'm older!'

'And beautiful.' His eyes seemed to concentrate, and she could discern a nerve beat under the tanned muscle of his strong throat. 'Twenty-two but still looking as young as when I first saw you.' He added enigmatically, 'It doesn't help much.'

For no reason she could pinpoint her heart began to pound erratically and she was terrified lest through the thin material of her nightclothes he would see it. Her chin lifted, her eyes defying him. 'Even if I don't look it, I am older and have long since outgrown the naïve, schoolgirlish habit of falling for every man who looks at me twice!'

She watched his expression, saw his eyes flicker and exulted at having caught him somewhere, she suspected below the belt. Or had she? His next words seemed to deny it.

'So I was one of the many? Of course it wasn't something I didn't discover.'

Too late she remembered Dicky, the man who used to be his brother-in-law. 'It never was how you thought,' she flung at him fiercely, her face flushing pink. Suddenly she was on her feet again, realising wildly that they couldn't seem to hold any kind of conversation without returning to this. It was like a festering sore that wouldn't heal, always there, when touched, to bring pain. 'You've always delighted in being able to think the worst of me,' she cried rashly, 'but I've learnt enough about men since I met you to know they aren't all alike!'

'So now you have some experience?'

She wasn't sure how to take that, but recklessly she nodded, 'Yes!'

Mark rose slowly to his feet, the whole six foot of him towering over her, swamping her, and without another word he deliberately reached out, drawing her to him, right into his arms. 'If you're so used to men,' his eyes glittered, 'one more can't make much difference. Remember I'm your boss, it wouldn't be too wise to fight me.'

The startled glance she raised became locked in the smouldering, unrelenting grey of his. As she watched, trance-like, unable to move, his eyes grew nearer, challenging her own before dissolving into flickering flames which threatened to devour her. In defence her heavy eyelids closed.

His kiss was all she had dreamed of in the last three years—and more. The contact of his mouth was hard and demanding as it fastened on hers. Last night he had been brutal. The pressure he exerted now wasn't gentle, but he allowed for her response. As he curved her to him the fire began gently, as a flickering flame before spreading through her entire body, leaping into devouring life.

Softly she moaned, but instead of fighting him as she had done before, she pressed her supple body against his, unwittingly adding fuel to his passion. His arms tightened and the trickle of excitement became a flood as his hands spread over her back and waist, as if he must have every part of her as close as possible. A blend of fear and rapture caught her, held her, causing her arms to lift, to cross behind his broad shoulders, her fingers to slide insistently through his crisp dark hair.

His head lifted and his expression made her tremble even while it thrilled. He looked so ruthless he might have decided never to let her go, and to her everlasting shame she wanted him to think this way, so she would have an excuse to surrender.

But as soon as the thought struck her she felt impelled to struggle, to deny such basic instincts which were surely foreign to her nature. 'Let me go, Mark!' she cried, when a few moments later she recovered sufficient breath.

The only reply she received was a low, mocking exclamation and her mouth taken again and explored with devastating thoroughness. 'I hate you!' she choked, a long while later.

'No, you don't.' He eased her away from him slightly, examining her flushed cheeks with satisfaction. 'You're enjoying this, my exotic little liar, as much as I am. I can sense the need in you.' He tilted her hot face up, running his mouth sensuously along the lovely line of her chin to her small ear. This he bit sharply as if in reprisal for her sins. 'How long is it, Sara, since a man really kissed you?'

Not since you did, Sara wanted to cry, but while the knowledge should have jarred it only seemed to bring home to her that without Mark Fenwick she was nothing. Never before had she felt like this about any man, consumed by a yearning so terrible as to make everything else seem unimportant.

'Sara!' He gave an exasperated groan when she didn't answer but merely tried to hide her too expressive face against him. He wouldn't let her, his hand was dominant beneath her chin as he stared down at her. 'You don't have to answer, darling, I can read all I want from your dark eyes—and your body. You have a delightful body, Sara, soft and warm and very enticing. Didn't you realise?'

She stiffened, clutching at a surge of indignation rather than the sensuous pleasure his words brought. 'Let me go, you're mistaken,' she entreated, trying to use her hands to push against his wide chest. He wore only a short-sleeved, casual shirt, open at the neck, and she only managed to dislodge a button while his powerful arms made nonsense of her struggles. 'Mark!' she almost begged.

His white teeth glinted, briefly amused and not sympathetic. As if to punish her afresh his hand went to the sash on her waist, unfastening her thin robe and sweeping it from her shoulders. Then, before she could move, he had thrust her silky nightdress aside and his mouth was exploring her bared breast. 'God, Sara,' his voice came harshly, 'it's been a long time! I've dreamt of this, it's haunted me, you can't know how I've regretted never possessing you!'

His passion overwhelmed her, her pulse raced as he tormented her, held her tightly, even savagely so she would have bruises in the morning. There was something about Mark that frightened even as it thrilled. He had never been a gentle lover, considerate perhaps, but never allowing her much respite. As if he knew exactly what she was capable of he drew her ruthlessly along with his deep expertise. Her mouth was crushed beneath his, her small, slender body, every curve of her hips and breast caressed, moulded against him as his passion mounted, until she only wanted to beg feverishly for him to do something, anything to ease the intolerable strain.

Then suddenly, just when it seemed his control was about to snap, he halted, as the glinting metal of his watch caught his vision as he briefly raised his head. 'Dolores!' the name was followed by a grim sigh. 'Damn, I almost forgot!'

'Dolores?' Sara's voice was only a hoarse whisper as she opened her eyes to stare blindly at his withdrawn face. She couldn't bear to let Mark go—not yet . . .

'I'm sorry, I have to meet her.' Quietly he disentangled Sara's clinging arms from about his neck. 'She's a friend of mine. A very important one, I'm afraid.'

'I see.' Silently Sara stood while he picked up her wrap and put it gently around her. She felt horribly sick. How could he turn passion on and off like this? What kind of a man was he that he could go straight from her arms into those of another girl? Easily, she supposed bitterly, holding a little conversation with herself while he watched her warily. His brilliance lay in the way he could extract himself from such situations, so calmly and with a matchless effrontery to leave her gasping.

'Don't you ever,' she cried wildly, 'call me a tramp again!'

'I wasn't going to,' he returned remotely, his eyes on her ashen face, 'but I still maintain you've the makings of a good one.'

Before she could collect a reply from the anger that flooded her, he turned and strode through the door.

The next morning Claude asked teasingly, 'Did your new boss find you last night?'

Sara blinked at him. 'So it was you?'

'If you mean was it I who told him where to find you, then the answer's yes.' Claude raised elegant eyebrows. 'You didn't imagine he would explain what he wanted to just anybody, did you, darling?'

'You didn't tell him you're my cousin, did you?'

'No, I didn't give myself the pleasure. He looked at me so suspiciously I decided not to.'

'Suspiciously?'

'Sure,' Claude drawled, 'but I might only have imagined it, darling.'

Sara was fifteen minutes late that morning, and not because of her head. Her bus broke down, and in the scramble for another she boarded the wrong one and had to change again. The ache in her head was barely detectable but that of her heart was another thing.

Mark, to her astonishment, looked livid when she walked in. 'Where on earth have you been?' he demanded coldly.

She had a suspicion he would have liked to use stronger language. As it was his tone more than made up for the missing expletives. Sara, seeing only hard indifference in his face, felt a vein of hurt begin to throb in her temple, and like the evening before she envied his apparent ability to turn his emotions on and off like a tap. She tried to explain about the bus, although, quite clearly, he had patience with none of her story. She was only too glad he didn't insist on knowing why she had got on the wrong one. After an evening with the glamorous Dolores he would be too distracted to enquire too closely into the dim-witted behaviour of his secretary. He returned to his office, slamming the door without bothering to ask if she'd quite recovered.

Sara tried not to look at him for the rest of the morning, attempting to get on with her work as though the scene in her bedroom the evening before had never happened. She felt grateful that she was able to present such a calmly dignified front. No one could guess, she was convinced, that each time she was near him her heartbeat accelerated so dramatically. Mark remained entirely indifferent as the morning continued, yet she found herself wondering. Was he really as uninterested as he appeared to wish her to think? Clearly he didn't mind kissing her, but with what in mind she wasn't sure. Punishment, perhaps, a continued reprisal for the hurt she had done his sister and employing the only method he could think of. Especially in the face of her apparent lack of true remorse. Sara trembled, then dismissed such illogical thoughts as ridiculous. Mark wasn't, she was sure, a man as vindictive as all that.

There was Dolores, however. She constituted a definite fact. Sara knew she couldn't be imagining her, as hadn't Mark mentioned Dolores himself? Hadn't he seen her on two consecutive evenings and said himself that she was important? It certainly proved she must be of more consequence to him than anyone else, and for the rest of the morning a vivid picture of a dark-eyed Southern beauty kept coming between Sara and her work, bringing a lump of unhappiness to her throat.

By lunchtime she was almost exhausted. Mark had kept her running all morning, and there had been, to add to everything else, a positive stream of staff to his office and, with some, her presence had been requested too.

After the last had departed Mark rang for her immediately. He wasn't going out to lunch himself, and while this didn't surprise her she fancied he waited with a sardonic glint in his eye as she rang down to the canteen for coffee and sandwiches. He insisted she used his phone and his eyes were on her all the time. Memories, they seemed to say; can't you remember that first lunch we shared so long ago?

Drat the man! Almost belligerently Sara stared at him, daring him to put such thoughts into words, challenging him to upset her further. She almost sighed with relief when he didn't remind her of that other occasion although the quirk at the corner of his mouth as he asked her to join him, betrayed he was tempted.

When she refused politely he merely sighed. 'Sit down, then, Miss Shaw. This won't take a minute but even a short rest might do you good. You look rather exhausted. How's the head?'

How like him to ask about that part of her which was suffering least! 'It's all right,' she muttered ungraciously, making a great thing of straightening her pad.

'You won't want that,' he observed laconically.

Seething, because temper seemed better than letting sick nerves take over, she waited, thinking there had been no need to hurry. In fact, peering closer, if she could believe it, he was merely doodling on a sheet of foolscap! With difficulty Sara restrained a sharp query, realising in time that if he chose to doodle it was not her place to complain. It was so out of character, though, that she felt perplexed.

Mark's eyes glinted as he glanced at her at last, as if he had deliberately given her the opportunity to study him. 'I'm just wondering,' he said innocently, 'If Hargreaves is quite reliable?'

'But of course he is!' she bristled immediately.

Mark's face was remote. 'What makes you think so?'

'Well—George, Mr Dent, always left him in charge when he had to be away and when he went on holiday.'

Mark's pen moved consideringly. 'Did he often go on holiday?'

'Oh yes. At least twice a year, not counting long weekends. He and his wife have no family, you see, as you must know.' Her voice trailed off, then gained momentum. 'This is why he went away more than perhaps some business men do. He considered his wife more important than a business he has no one to leave to.'

'Mrs Dent certainly appears to appreciate him.'

'Yes. I believe they are still very much in love.'

One of his dark brows rose ironically. 'You sound as if this surprises you. As if to go on caring for someone is impossible.'

'No, I don't think it would be impossible at all to love someone for ever and ever!'

Her cheeks went scarlet as she paused, aware of what she had just said, terrified he should suspect more than she wanted him to.

'Go on,' he said softly.

'I'm sorry,' she muttered, 'it's just that I feel worried that you aren't satisfied with Mr Hargreaves. You see, his wife has just had a baby and it would be rather dreadful if he lost his job.'

'Don't worry,' he rejoined wryly. 'Contrary to what you

appear to imagine I don't take exception to your defence of married happiness. How could I,' he grinned, 'with so much evidence around? Personally I'm quite willing to be converted.'

Was he referring to his relationship with the glamorous Dolores? The heat in Sara's cheeks dispersed coldly.

Mark continued, 'I wasn't really questioning Mr Hargreaves' ability. I merely wanted you to confirm a few things. He seems a very competent young man and not afraid of responsibility, just the sort to go a long way with a firm like Astro Chemicals. I'm considering leaving him in charge as I have to return to London.'

Bleak dismay rushing through her, Sara's gaze fell blankly to her hands. She might have guessed he wouldn't stay long. She waited for her first reaction to turn to relief, but the shaken feeling within her only increased. She managed to say, 'I understand.'

'Perhaps you don't,' he said quietly. 'I'm only going for a few days and I want you to come with me.'

The relief which came now seemed out of context and she could only stare.

Mark spoke gently, as if willing to be tolerant of her obvious confusion. 'You'll only be away two or three nights at the most.'

Suddenly she was alarmed. 'You can't mean you want me to go back to Astro's? To act as your secretary there?'

'Wouldn't you like to, Miss Shaw?' His eyes gleamed.

'No,' she almost gasped with dismay, 'oh, no, Mark, I couldn't!'

He put his handsome head back and laughed. 'You're a strange one, Sara. Wouldn't you care to bask in the reflected glory? Queen it over all your old friends—and enemies? Give the gossips something to really get their teeth into?'

'Oh, don't!' she begged anxiously, unsure whether he was teasing. 'You know I wouldn't know where to begin, and you'd only get impatient.'

'I can't guarantee my patience,' he agreed, 'but, on the

other hand, I refuse to doubt your ability. You have a bright intelligence, Sara, and would cope very well. However,' he frowned contemplatively, 'I don't want you back there myself, not perhaps until Miss Drew retires and I can offer you her job permanently.'

'I don't think I would accept such a job, even if you did offer it,' Sara replied carefully, wondering at his glint of satisfaction as she went pale. She knew she could never bear to work for years beside Mark as Miss Drew had done, merely as his secretary. Not feeling the way she did about him. Exactly how this was, Sara still refused to define. Hastily she asked, 'If you don't need me in your London office why do I have to come at all?'

'I want you there in case Hargreaves has any problems. He can get in touch with you at my house, which will save me being interrupted at the office, and we can work on his queries in the evening.'

'You mean you want me to stay at your home?'

'That's right. Don't look so worried, Miss Shaw, we can be as formal as you like. I have a housekeeper who makes a perfectly good chaperone, believe me. It's the only way I can think of to handle an extremely delicate situation. You must understand, Sara, if this wasn't very important to me I shouldn't ask it of you.'

Why did he sound as if there was a double meaning, a slight deviation which escaped her?

Mark was continuing laconically, 'If you'd really rather not, Sara, I can always ask someone else. It seems such a pity, though, as you'll know exactly what Hargreaves is talking about.'

Feeling trapped, Sara seemed to have no alternative but to agree.

Mark said smoothly, not trying to hide what looked suspiciously like a hint of satisfaction in his eyes. 'I've been in touch with the Criterion, notifying them that I shall be away and suggest you do the same. I'm retaining my suite as we shall be back by Friday at the latest. I'm sure your accommodation should be quite safe too, as I can't imagine anyone wanting such a poky little attic room.'

Swiftly Sara sprang to its defence. She was very fond of her room, which wasn't over-big, she was forced to admit, but was her own. Her aunt and uncle were always trying to get her to take a larger one, but she couldn't very well explain this to Mark. Besides, she would rather be tucked away under the eaves; she liked the feeling of remoteness. At least she had these past three years, since she first returned from London. No one had heard her then when she had wept. Hating even the memory of such weakness and regretting that the cause of it was so near, she almost snapped, 'My room is not poky!'

'Last night I must admit it was cosy!'

How could he refer to that! Had he no shame—holding her the way he had done, then going straight into the arms of another woman? Needles of colour ran painfully under Sara's satiny skin as she looked at him, shivering at his mockery. How was he going to do without his beautiful Dolores? She wouldn't, with all her commitments here in Coventry, be able to follow Mark to London. Sara felt a reprehensible flicker of satisfaction.

'You realise,' Mark's voice, still suave, cut through her thoughts, 'you won't be able to assist at the hotel until we return?'

'Oh!' She gave what she knew must have been almost a start of dismay. 'I can always,' she rushed on rashly, 'make up for it next week. They're particularly busy just now.'

'Really?' his cool, distant tones reminded her of their recent arguments on this subject and her colour deepened.

'They wouldn't throw me out,' she exclaimed, with a regrettable smugness, 'even if I never did another thing! I can make up for my absence in other ways.'

To her surprise Mark's jaw went tight and his eyes cold. 'That young manager, perhaps, doesn't mind what he takes in lieu of payment for a room.'

Furiously, Sara jumped to her feet, her blue eyes sparkling. 'I don't know quite what you mean by that, Mr Fenwick, but it sounds nasty!'

He too rose, his temper on a more even keel but stronger. 'Not as nasty as I can get, so be warned, Sara. There are many things about your position there which don't altogether please me! Now go and do your packing. I'll pick you up in a couple of hours. That should give you plenty of time.'

CHAPTER NINE

IT was lovely to be awakened next morning with a cup of tea. It was on her bedside cabinet and the sharp click when the housekeeper closed the door must have aroused her. That click had sounded rather disapproving and, glancing at her watch, Sara saw it was after nine. The housekeeper obviously thought it was too late for someone in Sara's position. She perhaps didn't know that Mark had told her not to worry about sleeping in as there would be little possibility of John Hargreaves ringing before ten at the earliest.

Last night on the way here Mark had been coolly distant, although he had talked idly from time to time. Sipping her hot tea, after deciding not to be too worried by Mrs Oliver's abruptness, Sara recalled that most of what he had said had been impersonal.

Coventry, as a city, apparently interested him very much. Sara suspected he would be interested in his surroundings wherever he went and she was glad she could answer most of his questions. This was chiefly because of her father who, as an eminent historian, had been intensely interested in old cities. It seemed to earn Mark's respect that though the centre of Coventry had been almost completely destroyed by bombs in November 1940, it had been rebuilt to form the gracious city it was today.

Initially it was an old city, with many historical associations, if its present ones were more in connection with the motor industry, aeroplanes, plastics and the like. Soldiers during the Civil War had been sent to Coventry as a suitable punishment, hence the old saying which still survived.

'I think I'd be more interested in Lady Godiva's ride,' Mark had teased. 'Didn't her husband, Leofric, promise to reduce taxes if she rode naked through the streets?'

'Well, she succeeded,' Sara retorted, her cheeks slightly pink.

'Hmm, I wonder if our present Chancellor could be so persuaded?' Mark had retorted, tongue in cheek.

'There's the new theatre, the Belgrade,' she had hastened, then paused, the pink in her cheeks flaming. What on earth had possessed her to mention this? If Dolores was taking part in a show there he must know all about it, and would probably think she was fishing. He could be right! 'There are other places,' she had rushed on.

'Should any one place interest me particularly?' he had asked, so smoothly that Sara had known immediately that he saw through her small subterfuge.

She hadn't answered but glanced at him swiftly, watching out of the corner of her eye as he drove on competently. Not for the world would she have confessed she liked watching him. There was no denying his virile masculinity, although it was never the obvious kind. He was controlled, disciplined, but a few minutes in his arms had taught her more than any other man might, in the same number of hours. She had fallen silent, dreaming while trying not to, and considered with mixed feelings Mark's next query.

'Do you come to London often, Sara?'

'No.' She didn't want to tell him she had never been back since she'd left Astro's.

But he dug further. 'When were you last there?'

'Three years ago.' Forced into a corner, she let the truth come out baldly.

'So!' Mark whistled under his breath for a few moments, but while Sara stiffened against further comment it never came. He had merely put out his hand and started playing with her fingers.

As if paralysed she had let him, until she had remembered it had been like this when she had first met him, when she had allowed him to treat her as his mood moved him. Swiftly she had snatched her hand away, too aware of a twinge of disappointment that he made no effort to retain it.

In London he had brought her straight here to his house before leaving immediately for his office. When he had gone nostalgia had momentarily gripped her at the thought of that huge building which had confused her for weeks. Curiously she had wondered what Gwen and the others were doing. She hadn't cared to ask Mark, but now she was here there could surely be no harm in enquiring how they were. The only thing she was strangely reluctant to do was meet them.

The bedroom Mark had allocated her was beautiful, the deep cream carpet and rose-covered wallpaper, the softly draped bed presenting luxurious comfort. Sara felt more like a princess than an ordinary secretary, and had to keep reminding herself she was the latter. The evening before she had gone to bed early. Mark hadn't returned until late and had looked slightly harassed. After dinner he hadn't even waited to take coffee with her but disappeared into his study and hadn't emerged. She had read until about ten, trying to ignore a prevailing feeling of neglect and having to assure herself she was on a business trip, not a vacation. Shortly afterwards she had gone to bed and lain listening for Mark's footsteps on the stairs. Footsteps which had never come, long after the hall clock struck midnight.

John Hargreaves rang several times during the day, but there wasn't anything important. Sara was able to help him herself, although she made notes of each call to show Mark when he came in. By five she felt quite irritated, with the awful suspicion that there was some kind of conspiracy. She was sure she could have helped John as well in Coventry as here, and that most of the queries she had answered need not have been asked in the first place!

When Mark arrived at half past six and told her he was taking her out to dinner and a show, she almost gaped at him.

'I—you said we were to work?'

'I did check,' he smiled. 'John doesn't appear to have any

problems you haven't coped with nicely.'

'As any child might have done,' she retorted icily.

He glanced at her hostile face comprehendingly. 'But there might have been, Sara. You must accept this. We've been fortunate so far. I've told you before, this is a very critical time and I can't do with small irritations. As it is we have an even larger merger coming off and my chairman is absolutely breathing down my neck, but,' he hesitated briefly, 'that's another story. Go and change, like a good girl. No more argument.'

'I am changed,' she retorted quickly, not sure she should give in so easily in spite of what he said. 'I expected a working evening.'

He frowned, his eyes on her navy skirt and white blouse, trim but not very party-like. 'Don't tell me,' he grinned, 'you haven't succumbed to the usual feminine habit of packing something extra pretty, just in case?'

Sara had. It consisted of flimsy layers of soft polyester crêpe-de-chine in lovely shades of blue. When she had seen it she hadn't been able to resist it, but it had hung unworn in her wardrobe for weeks.

'Go and put it on.' Mark's smile deepened maddingly as he read her guilty face. 'Remember I'm the boss.'

'Not for much longer,' she retorted bravely, while feeling obliged to obey him. When he looked at her like that all her arguments melted like snow in the sun.

'You could be right,' he sighed ruefully. 'One of these days you might easily be calling the tune, if I don't watch out.'

Sara didn't wait to puzzle that one out. She was ready very quickly, for all her indignation, spending more time wondering where Mark was taking her than regretting a quiet evening at home. It was only after being in all day, she assured herself; naturally she felt like a change of scene. It wasn't simply because of Mark! She had wondered about dinner, not having caught the aroma of anything cooking, but the housekeeper, though nice, seemed a bit of a martinet and she hadn't liked to ask. Sara suspected Mrs Oliver didn't quite know what to make of her being here, but she had remembered her from three years ago. Sara had somehow felt pleased about that.

Looking in the mirror she felt a strange shiver of surprise rise to her throat. How she wished her parents could have seen the slim, graceful girl reflected there. She didn't feel so very young any more and regretted that she still looked it, but, while not sure she approved of herself, she knew instinctively her parents would have done.

'You look beautiful,' said Mark, staring at her intently, something dangerous smouldering in the back of his grey eyes. Sara was reminded of other evenings when he had told her so, only this time she felt something deeper. It was as if something inside him was reaching out to take her over and he was restraining himself with difficulty.

Mocking inwardly, Sara derided herself for being so fanciful, too nostalgic. But if the future wasn't to contain Mark—and for her it couldn't—then she would rather go back in time, even if such reminiscence hurt.

Mark looked devastatingly handsome in evening dress, so dark and purposeful as to almost take her breath away. If she hadn't been so frightened of getting hurt again, of having to undergo so much torture, she might have enjoyed having him for an escort that evening.

To her surprise he took her to one of the same restaurants where they had dined and danced several times before. He must have chosen it deliberately, and she wondered why. This one she had particularly liked, but he made no reference to the fact or gave any indication that he himself remembered. The play he took her to afterwards was a sparkling, light-hearted comedy which nevertheless had its deeper moments. Sara's pulse raced when in one of these he took her hand, which seemed to be becoming a habit of his, and held it firmly. He held it for the greater part of the last act, his fingers slipping disconcertingly over her wrist to her hurrying pulse before he released her. As he did so she felt his narrowed glance on her averted profile, but she refused to look at him.

It was after midnight when they got in. There seemed something so husband and wife-like about returning together like this from an evening out that Sara sighed, even as she rejected such thoughts with impatience. This didn't, however, stop her from wondering wistfully if Mark would want to kiss her goodnight. He hadn't been completely averse to kissing her in the past.

Lingering, perhaps a little too obviously, near the bottom of the stairs as he looked up, she caught his slightly enigmatical glance as he turned. 'I think,' he gave a sardonic smile, 'you're in need of hot milk, or cocoa, then bed.'

'No, thank you,' she protested quickly, thinking ruefully that in spite of her efforts to give an impression of sophistication he merely associated her with hot milk and cocoa! Yet surely she didn't really want more? It was becoming too familiar, this longing within her to be in his arms. Rather too loudly, as he hesitated, she went on, 'We haven't discussed the various items Mr Hargreaves enquired about, and I might not see you in the morning.'

'I'll just have to see you in the morning, won't I?'

'Couldn't we . . .'

Deviously he must have guessed what was really on her mind, as he turned her firmly towards the stairs. 'Look, Sara, I'm not in the mood for coffee and platonic kisses with Mr Hargreaves sandwiched in between. You'd be much wiser to go to bed.'

Coffee and kisses—he had a nerve! Shaken to something near anger, she stared up at him. 'That was a beastly thing to say, and the last thing I was thinking of,' she lied blatantly.

'Good,' he retorted crisply, 'because I don't intend supplying them.'

'Oh!' She flushed scarlet, but afraid of what he might read in her too-transparent face, she turned and fled. It seemed no consolation that only his softly derisive laughter followed her upstairs.

Sara dreamt that night that they were at the cottage again, she and Mark, drinking champagne in front of a roaring fire in the lounge. It was warm in the firelight and outside a cold wind blew. Afterwards Mark picked her up and carried her upstairs. She could see his face, very tender and possessive, very sensuous as he strode with her into the bedroom and gently closed the door. But there was nothing very gentle in his face after that. It was passionate and alive, taut with desire as he laid her down. Over and over he murmured, 'I love you.'

Just before his lips met hers she woke up. For a moment she was flooded with frustrated disappointment on realising it had all been a dream. Then, with a cry almost of shame, she turned over and buried her hot face in the pillows.

The next time she woke it was to sober reality, yet there was something to make her heart pound again as she saw Mark coming over the carpet towards her, a tray in his hand. He wore, so far as her sleep-confused gaze could make out, only a short, navy towelling robe and a smile.

He put the tray down beside her. 'Just to prove it wasn't my intention to deprive you of anything last night,' he said inscrutably. 'But I warn you I won't make a habit of spoiling you like this. I did look in yesterday morning, but you were fast asleep and Mrs Oliver, deliberately I think, forestalled me with your tea.'

Sara sat up with a start, still muddled. 'Where is she this morning?' she gasped. Then, inconsistently, 'It surely can't be morning already? What time is it?'

'Only seven-thirty and, as Mrs Oliver never appears until the stroke of eight, it seems a shame to let good tea go to waste.'

'Oh!' More confused than ever, Sara struggled up on one elbow, overlooking that she had very little to cover her but an extremely brief nightie. 'Do you think she would approve of you bringing me tea?'

The angle of his head suggested he was arrogant enough to disregard anything Mrs Oliver chose to think. He didn't even bother to answer. 'Move over,' he commanded, with an equal disregard for Sara's fluttering pulse as he dropped down on the edge of the bed beside her. 'I've brought a cup for myself so we can discuss anything you feel necessary while we drink it.'

'Yes—I see.' Suddenly realising her state of undress, she fumbled, her cheeks pink, to cover herself adequately with the sheet, her eyes unconsciously measuring the distance to where her wrap lay discarded over a chair.

He grunted lazily. 'I'd make do with the sheet,' he advised. 'You'll find it more comfortable. I don't plan, not this time, to spend the whole day. Besides, I'm getting used to seeing you in a state of undress.'

Her cheeks went pinker still and she tried to concentrate on her tea, attempting to block out the image of Mark, so darkly masculine in his navy robe, with the dark shadow of a night's growth on his chin—something which only seemed to add to his attraction.

He rubbed his chin ruefully as he caught her gaze. 'You don't mind, do you, Sara?'

It sounded so intimate somehow that her glance dropped from the turmoil within her. Had he meant to give exactly that impression? she wondered, trying not to think chaotically what such roughness might do to her tender skin. How she might not care ...

Her uncertain silence seemed to prompt him to supply an explanation. 'I'm afraid worry over Hargreaves precipitated me towards your door more urgently than I might otherwise have done.'

Was she supposed to believe that? It came out too pat! She couldn't imagine Mark losing sleep over anyone, least of all John Hargreaves!

'I hope you haven't been having nightmares about him too?' Mark added, with a grin.

'It wasn't him, it was you!' she spluttered without meaning to, her face scarlet with mortification.

The odd quirk at the side of Mark's mouth deepened before he suddenly sobered, draining his cup with a sigh. His eyes went over her, lingering on her tumbled hair, her face, devoid of make-up but very beautiful in spite of that. 'What a child you still are—and look. About seventeen!'

'I can't help that.'

'No,' turning, he rested his arm across the bed, appraising her moodily, 'I don't suppose you can. What makes a woman look older, I wonder? A hundred lovers? Certainly a lack of them presents an enticing if rather frightening image, although it does appear to keep the years at bay.'

Sara flinched, resentful that he should always be so scornful of her limited experience. He might not say so outright, but his derision was always there. 'You came to discuss Mr Hargreaves' problems, not mine,' she reminded him fiercely.

'Ah, yes,' Mark murmured, the glint in his eye deepening mockingly.

For the next ten minutes he appeared to concentrate on Mr Hargreaves, giving her bits of advice to pass on, odd information that hadn't occurred to her. 'Do the same today,' he advised, 'but don't stay in all the time. I'd like you to get some fresh air, otherwise you'll be so pale when you return to Coventry they'll wonder what I've been doing with you. Go to the park.'

'If you like,' she agreed, trying to speak evenly, aware that he hadn't moved his eyes from her face for quite a while. He was too close and she stirred uneasily, though more nervous of her own reactions than his. 'You'll be back tonight, I expect,' she spoke to his raised eyebrows, not really following what he said as she stared at him, her mind going back distractingly to the dream she had had. This might well be a continuation, a beginning, or end, she wasn't sure which. Her blue eyes widened, seeming to lose themselves in the smouldering greyness of Mark's. His eyes so often reminded her of cool northern skies until a moment like this.

'Sara,' he drew a strand of her silky hair through his fingers, startling her. Then his hands moved, coming down to grip her bare, satiny shoulders, bringing her up towards him. He kissed her gently, without passion, and for a moment she was able to resist. Then the light pressure of his mouth deepened demandingly and she found herself clinging to him, responding with increasing passion.

He murmured something, an odd expression in his eyes, part triumph, part surprise as his head lifted fractionally.

'Are you trying to say something, Mark?' she whispered.

'Don't be so curious, Sara Shaw. Perhaps it's better you don't know, not yet.' His mouth came down again, making further speech impossible as his lips trailed tenderly from her neck to her shoulders from which he unhurriedly slipped the straps of her thin nightgown. Her thick lashes fell as he watched her rapt face and his mouth lowered to seek her bare breasts.

He grasped one of her small hands, pushing it through the open front of his robe, as if it gave him great pleasure to have it there. Breathing quickly, she let it lie, then moved it experimentally over his broad, hair-covered chest, feeling the heavy beat of his heart quickening under her tentative fingers.

When his mouth at last returned to hers he looked shaken and his lips were rough, dealing far from gently with her own as he pulled her closer, holding her hard against him until her head swam. His hands moving over her were sensuous, arousing, and his skin was hot against hers as naked desire raged like a sweeping, devastating storm between them. His mouth eased, his lips tormenting. 'When are you going to give me what I want, Sara? You can't surely deny this thing between us any longer?'

It was only with difficulty that Sara spoke at all. Her head was swimming, her limbs like water. She could barely think clearly. 'You've always rejected me, Mark. You know that.'

'I'm not now,' he said thickly, his mouth assaulting her

eyes, her throat, her childishly curved mouth. 'I want to possess every part of you, your lovely body, your fascinating, illogical mind. Darling . . .'

To Sara's horror, as she listened, tears stung her eyes and rolled down her flushed cheeks to her mouth.

He went pale, his glance suddenly intent, his face taut. 'Sara,' he spoke urgently, 'we must talk, you and I. We can't go on——' Whatever else he had been about to say was cut off abruptly as a door banged distantly. 'Oh, lord,' he groaned, 'my dear housekeeper! And what I want to say won't bear interruption, not even the rattle of porridge plates!'

'Mark—please . . .'

'Never mind, darling,' he dropped a rueful kiss on her trembling mouth, 'I'll see you tonight. Until then, wait for me. Promise?'

Unable for some unfathomable reason to stop a flow of tears, she whispered, 'Yes, Mark,' helplessly. She wasn't sure whether he was pleased or angry at her obvious weakness, but somehow she didn't care. He had, for a few seconds, been utterly gentle with her, almost as if he really cared. Whatever he had to say later couldn't take this away from her.

There was an old tune which ran like that; Sara had heard it played at the hotel. Now she hummed it under her breath as she bathed and dressed, as she tried to forget the shame of her abandoned behaviour, attempted to ignore the delight. Carefully she chose a high-necked blouse so as to hide the red marks left by Mark's mouth, his roughened chin.

Satisfied that she looked very cool and composed, she ran downstairs, almost ready to face another day of Mr Hargreaves. Some time in the future she resolved to ask Mark if Mr Hargreaves had been absolutely necessary, as he would have her think. For the moment she was prepared to leave it. 'Sufficient unto the day,' she murmured, as she reached the hall.

Mark had already gone and as Sara ate her solitary breakfast, Mrs Oliver padded in and out of the dining room, seeing to her every need. Sara felt like insisting she could manage without such a degree of attention, but she didn't think Mrs Oliver would approve.

She did carry out her own dishes and washed them up, ignoring Mrs Oliver's tongue-clicking. 'I've little else to do,' Sara said mildly. 'If Mr Hargreaves rings from Coventry I can hear him from here.'

Mrs Oliver nodded, she even smiled and began chatting. It was only about the weather, but Sara decided it was a step in the right direction. When Mrs Oliver told her Mr Fenwick wouldn't be in to lunch, Sara didn't say she had known. Instead she asked Mrs Oliver not to bother preparing any for her as she would have sandwiches in the park. At this, Mrs Oliver immediately offered to make them herself.

'Mr Fenwick would be annoyed if I let you go without anything,' she continued firmly. 'I expect he won't be very pleased as it is, because he left orders to make you something filling.' From Mrs Oliver's expression it was clear that she secretly agreed that Sara could do with some fattening up, but she did look slightly mollified when Sara accepted with a grateful smile.

In spite of her walk in the park and a delightful if slightly extravagant packed lunch, the day dragged. There was no crisis at the Coventry office, John only rang once, and Mrs Oliver was out most of the afternoon. The house was quiet and while Sara would have been less than human not to have appreciated the luxury of her surroundings she felt curiously on edge.

To her surprise Mark rang later in the afternoon, but just to say he wouldn't be home until around seven. He hoped she didn't mind.

'No, of course not.' Tension made her voice go stiff and she was aware of his sharply contemplative pause.

'Are you all right, Sara?'

'Yes, yes, of course!' but her voice was unusually shrill. She knew it and wished fervently she had tried harder to control it. She could sense Mark holding the receiver away from his ear, his puzzled frown. Quickly, before he could begin asking questions, she said, 'I've been in the park. I've scarcely got my breath back.'

'I'd like to remove it completely—well, almost.' His tones menaced lightly over the line and her heart raced as she almost felt his arms around her.

She tried to be sensible. 'I'd better go now, Mark, John Hargreaves might be waiting.'

'So I must continue to play second fiddle to another man!'

'Goodbye, Mark.'

Her fingers trembled as she replaced the telephone and sank into a nearby chair. Mark had sounded almost proprietorial, and she'd be a fool to think he wasn't to some degree attracted, but how far could she trust his feelings? Remembering the hurt she had suffered, she shivered, doubting she could face it again. Maybe he would just like an affair, but she didn't think she had the right personality for that. She wasn't sure how she would have felt if her feelings hadn't been involved. Such immunity might have protected her from further hurt when he grew tired of her, but it seemed too late for that now. She was too much in love with him. Loving him as she did she dared not, would not trust him! Somehow she must keep him at arm's length, though how she was to manage this she had no idea.

It was just before seven when Mark came in. Sara heard his key in the door and sat waiting, willing herself not to run and meet him.

He came immediately into the lounge, pausing in the doorway, the warmth of his eyes fading a little as he saw her trim but exceedingly businesslike navy skirt and blouse. 'Good heavens,' he muttered, half under his breath, 'why that get-up?'

Flushing painfully, Sara seemed unable to meet his flinty stare.

'So,' suddenly he was softly formidable, 'you're still afraid to trust me? This is a kind of armour against any attempt to seduce you. Well, I can't say I wasn't tempted.'

It was much worse than she had expected. His slow anger was terrible, more especially so because she couldn't bring herself to act naturally. Every muscle in her body seemed horribly taut and she was conscious that the hectic flush on her cheeks must denote all kinds of things she never intended. 'You said,' she stammered, 'we were staying in. I didn't think you'd want me to dress up.'

'I like to see women looking feminine in the evening. But I think you already know that, Miss Shaw!'

Anger was fast replacing fright as he sneered at her. She realised, from the tired lines on his face, he had had a busy day, but this surely didn't give him the right to insult her! It made things worse that she had a niggling suspicion he was right. Yet it could never be wise to tell him so. As evenly as possible she said, 'I haven't anything but what I wore last night and I thought it rather festive for this occasion.'

'What occasion?' he ground out so sarcastically she almost shrank.

'You know what I meant,' she faltered.

'I'm not sure that I do,' he replied cruelly. Then, 'What about that nice little number you wore to come here in? If you dislike the idea of dressing up for me, that wasn't too bad.'

Sara's blue eyes darkened anxiously, her faint temper fading. She had forgotten about it—or had she been so busy concentrating on something to discourage him that subconsciously she had deliberately overlooked it? As she saw how her uncertainty appeared to be irritating Mark beyond everything, her heart sank. Even with the most expensive dresses in the world could she ever have been the kind of woman he enjoyed being seen with? The smart, ultra-sophisticated type, always looking as though they had stepped straight from a beauty parlour. 'I'm sorry,' was all she could think of to say.

'Your apology might be charming if it wasn't so obviously reluctant.' Mark's voice was frigid.

'I think,' Sara began distractedly, not able to bear the way he looked at her, 'I think Mrs Oliver will have dinner ready soon.'

His mouth curled. 'You sound very like an established hostess! I assure you I'm fully conversant with the times of meals in my own house!'

'I'm sorry,' she said again, feeling horribly like crawling into a corner and hiding her head. All her three years of striving after a certain worldliness seemed wasted; she felt even more naïve than she had when she first had known Mark. Then she had hated it when he had glanced at her as coldly as he did now. But it had never seemed as bad as this and she wondered why they should be quarrelling so bitterly. What had happened since this morning? Or was it entirely her fault? If she had set out to intentionally antagonise Mark by her own foolish stiffness then she was succeeding beyond her wildest hopes. If only it didn't hurt so that he was obviously willing to meet her more than half-way!

If she had any pity to spare, however, she suspected she might be wiser to keep it for herself, as his indifferent shrug was wounding beyond everything. 'I don't know what I'm making such a fuss about,' he said curtly. 'I have more than enough to keep me busy for the whole of the evening in my study. I don't need to look at you at all.'

'Mark——!' she began, her face white.

It was at that moment that the doorbell rang and, as if glad to escape, Mark went to see who was there himself.

'Darling!' Sara heard a melodious feminine voice, and through the open door, saw Mark enveloped in a swirl of expensive summer furs. 'As soon as I received your message I came!'

Sara didn't catch Mark's reply as he disentangled himself and quickly closed the door between them. He needn't have bothered, she thought bleakly, understanding now the reason for his behaviour since he came in. It was painfully clear that he regretted the incident in Sara's bedroom that morning and had set out to disillusion her before this woman, whoever she was, arrived. Frozen, Sara stayed exactly where she was until, some time later, Mrs Oliver came to tell her dinner was served.

Not quite knowing what to expect, she was startled to find Mark, now smartly attired in a faultlessly cut dinner jacket, having drinks with a stranger in the hall. Sara's dazed eyes took in the woman's sultry beauty, her exotic make-up, the expensive perfume. She tried to smile but failed. Not that either of them appeared to notice.

'Ah, Dolores,' Mark's voice contained a soft note of boredom, 'here comes my secretary. Miss Shaw has been helping out in an emergency.'

So this was Dolores Juarez, the woman he had been seeing so much of in Coventry. Numbly Sara held out her hand, only to have it ignored as Miss Juarez merely inclined her head. Sara's hand dropped back nervously to her side. Miss Juarez had obviously decided meek little secretaries warranted only brief recognition.

'If you're ready, Dolores,' Mark smiled sardonically, 'we can go in. Miss Shaw will join us.'

Dolores looked surprised and obviously just restrained herself from suggesting that Sara dine in the kitchen with the rest of the staff. That Mark held out Sara's chair and waited until she was seated before doing so himself, she appeared to view with equal displeasure. She took very little notice of Sara throughout the meal, apart from the odd remark when Mark, deliberately it seemed, included Sara in the general conversation. Yet Sara saw that Dolores might be very attractive and not nearly so chilly as she at first seemed. It was very apparent that she had a fondness for Mark.

Sara recognised her as a star of some international standing, though she didn't seem to recall her being very widely acknowledged. In her husky, heavily accented English she remarked to Sara that it was too terrible to be compelled to do repertory in places like Coventry when London was much more her scene.

Mark flashed her an amused look. 'You shouldn't be complaining of Coventry, Dolores. It's Miss Shaw's home town.'

'Oh, you poor child!' Dolores sounded sympathetic, but her eyes narrowed as if she was suddenly suspicious. 'I don't know what I should have done there without Mark,' she added coolly.

Sara said nothing but looked down at her sweet, a delicious concoction of fresh fruits and cream which seemed to lose its taste. She had felt a little resentful when Dolores ignored her, now she almost prayed she would do so again!

Dolores didn't; she appeared to enjoy Sara's discomfiture. 'How do you like working for Mark, Miss Shaw? Does he bully you?'

'Oh, no—well——' Sara was chagrined to feel her cheeks flushing.

'Miss Shaw,' Mark cut in suavely, 'doesn't really enjoy working for me at all. I believe she suspects me of being a bit of a philanderer.'

'But a very charming one,' Dolores smiled. 'If you were a little older, Miss Shaw, you would appreciate that Mr Fenwick is a wonderful man!'

Inwardly Sara sat suffering, and growing furious at the same time! How could Mark sit there lapping it up? Was this what he meant by liking his women feminine? Unhappily she intercepted Dolores' languishing glance, the long white hand laid on his arm. She shivered as she remembered his tender passion earlier, scarcely able to apprehend that it had ever happened. Now he sat staring at her, his grey eyes hooded, taunting her as if she was someone he disliked. How right she had been not to trust him!

It didn't seem to matter that this was exactly what he had accused her of. Sara felt she would never find it possible to trust him again.

When the strangely uncomfortable meal was over, Mark announced that he and Dolores were going out. The hours of hard work in the study had apparently been shelved.

As Dolores departed to powder her nose, he spoke to Sara. 'I doubt if I'll see you again before you return to Coventry. I'm sending someone to take you back there tomorrow. I won't be going back myself until next week.'

He sounded stilted, too formal, but Sara didn't take this in. She could only stare. In spite of his recent coldness she couldn't quite believe he was so keen to be rid of her, and her eyes went huge with shock. 'I suppose,' she whispered indiscreetly, 'this is because of Miss Juarez. You want my room?'

He went colder still, his mouth set. 'You little fool!' he began, then stopped abruptly. 'We won't discuss Miss Juarez, if you don't mind.'

'You never want to discuss other women, do you?' she flared, unforgivably it seemed, judging from his expression.

'Sara!' he menaced, taking a step nearer, grasping one of her arms with fingers of steel, temper driving him. 'I'm warning you!'

Hastily she gulped, unconsciously striving after normality. 'I'm sorry, Mark. If I go back to Coventry, and I will if you want me to, how about Mr Hargreaves?'

'I think he'll be able to manage,' Mark replied indifferently, letting her go abruptly as Dolores called his name from the hall.

Just before he went he turned to gaze down at Sara's ashen face. It seemed he was about to say something, something he felt urgently, then, as if suddenly changing his mind, he walked away from her grimly, quickly closing the door.

CHAPTER TEN

SARA decided not to go back to Coventry next morning. She was, in fact, due for a long weekend and decided to take it. It was Friday and she doubted very much if Mark would return himself before the following week, especially as Mr Hargreaves appeared to be coping. There would be little for her to do and if Mark liked the idea of her sitting repenting her sins then he could think again! She would ring John Hargreaves and tell him what she intended doing, but she wouldn't get in touch with Mark. This would be too much like asking his permission and she refused to do this. He could be vexed or pleased; she was tired of being used like a doormat!

Overlooking that, as an employee, she could have certain obligations, Sara waited until she was sure Mark had gone before venturing downstairs. She fancied he was much later than usual but put this down to him having had a late night with Miss Juarez. It hadn't been all that late, just after eleven when he had come in alone, Sara had heard him as she had lain awake. He had come straight upstairs. There had been no voices and his footsteps had actually paused outside her door, and she was sure Miss Juarez had not been with him.

As she had already packed the night before, there wasn't much left to do. The few things still to go in her case she pushed in untidily, aware but uncaring that she might regret this when she found somewhere to stay. At the moment it didn't seem important that her clothes might be crumpled. Nothing seemed to matter any more, but this time she hoped she had finally learnt her lesson and would be able to forget Mark.

Downstairs she found breakfast waiting, with the fragrant

smell of fresh coffee on the air. Sara hesitated, anxious to be gone before anyone came to collect her but reluctant to offend Mrs Oliver, who had been extremely kind. 'I didn't intend staying for breakfast,' Sara faltered. 'I must go at once, I'm afraid.'

'But not before breakfast,' Mrs Oliver insisted firmly. 'Mr Fenwick left definite orders.'

Bother Mr Fenwick and his orders, Sara felt like saying, but wasn't sure if she could trust herself to say so without bursting into tears. And it would merely sound childish.

Reluctantly she sat down, sipping orange juice, refusing porridge, trying half-heartedly to eat a little of the beautifully cooked bacon and eggs but unable to swallow more than a mouthful.

Mrs Oliver watched her white face with alarm, viewing her lack of appetite with grave misgivings. Mark must have told her something about the arrangements he had made, or was making, for she said, 'It's a mercy you haven't to go catching trains—you don't look up to it, miss.'

'I'm quite all right, thank you,' Sara wrapped her hands tightly around her coffee cup, 'I never did have much colour. I wonder if you could tell this man who is coming to collect me that I won't be needing him? I've decided not to go back to Coventry today, you see.'

'Oh.' Mrs Oliver quite clearly didn't know what to make of this. 'Are you sure, dear? Mr Fenwick didn't mention this to me. I think he expects you to go straight home.'

'I haven't seen Mr Fenwick this morning,' Sara shrugged deviously.

'If you'd been five minutes earlier you would have done. I've never known him take so long in getting out. It's a pity you missed him.'

It's just as well I did, Sara thought. 'I expect he was tired after being out with Miss Juarez.'

'Ah, yes, that lady ...' Mrs Oliver didn't look too impressed, and Sara felt a traitorous leap of gladness in her heart.

'Is she staying here?' Sara realised she should have been ashamed of asking such a question. That she wasn't should have alarmed her but didn't. She might as well hear the worst, she was prepared for it! Mark might not be officially engaged to Miss Juarez, but he must be considering marrying her if he had sent for her to come here specially. Again Sara heard Dolores' voice.

'I came, darling, as soon as I received your message.'

No one could disregard the relevance of that! Mark must have sent for Dolores yesterday morning, perhaps as soon as he'd left Sara's bedroom. Recalling her tears, Sara knew Mark must have decided to deal with the situation in a way he thought better for them all. It hurt, but it had taught a much needed, if brutal lesson!

'I'm sorry, Mrs Oliver?' She became aware that the woman was saying something.

'It's all right, dear. I only said Miss Juarez is not staying here at the moment, but she did mention to me last night, when I happened to meet her on the stairs before she and Mr Fenwick went out, that she might be.'

'I understand.' Sara swallowed the last of her coffee with difficulty and jumped to her feet. No use prolonging the agony! Gravely she shook Mrs Oliver by the hand, thanking her for being so kind.

'It's been a real pleasure to look after you, miss,' Mrs Oliver assured her, as she saw her anxiously out.

Sara hailed a cab which took her a short but safe distance away, then rang Gwen. She didn't want to have to go personally to the offices and tried to time her call to coincide with what she hoped was still Gwen's coffee break. She might not be very popular, but it seemed imperative to speak to her. Recalling the way in which she had so abruptly left the office three years ago, without any proper goodbye, Sara felt there was a possibility that Gwen might not want to have anything more to do with her.

She was relieved and thankful when Gwen came to the phone almost immediately and seemed delighted that Sara had got in touch. After the first preliminaries, when Sara said rather tersely that she would be staying in London over the weekend, Gwen offered to put her up.

It appeared, since Sara had left, she had been married, and her naval officer husband was away at sea. 'We've just managed to get a super flat, darling, but it needs doing up. I'm making a start this weekend, so you can help me.'

Somehow to Sara it seemed the ideal solution. Things couldn't have turned out better. Gwen's flat was basically in good condition and pleasantly situated in a charming little cul-de-sac, but there was obviously a lot of interior decorating to be done. The hard work certainly prevented Sara being too conscious of her aching heart.

On Saturday morning they chose wallpaper and paint, Sara's natural flair for such things coming in handy. They worked throughout the weekend with Gwen declaring the flat would soon look like something out of *Homes and Gardens*! Feeling unable to leave Gwen with so much to finish, Sara got on with the painting while Gwen was at the office at the beginning of the week. On Wednesday she reluctantly told her she would have to return to Coventry next morning.

'I'll catch an early train,' she smiled sleepily, as they drank a last cup of tea before going to bed. She felt tired out but glad of it. 'I'm afraid I hadn't realised so much of the week has gone. If I don't go now there might be no job to go back to.'

'Would you mind so much?' Gwen asked.

'Probably not,' Sara confessed. Gwen knew that her firm had been taken over by Astro Chemicals and that Mark was there.

'We still can't understand why M.F. went to Coventry,' Gwen ruminated for the second time. 'It's still a mystery.'

It wouldn't be for much longer, Sara thought, not when the press got to know of his close alliance with Dolores Juarez. It could only be a matter of time.

'I expect he'll be getting married,' she sighed, her voice

unconsciously bleak as she continued her thoughts aloud.

'Married?' Gwen exclaimed, ears pricking. 'Oh, well, I suppose you could be right. Miss Gregg is convinced there's a woman in it somewhere, even if old Drew continues to be cagey. We're sure there must be some reason other than the obvious to send him up there. But if he's chasing his Lady Godiva he doesn't appear to have caught her yet.'

Sara tried to smile, as she was obviously meant to appreciate the joke.

'Who's acting as his secretary in Coventry?' Gwen suddenly wanted to know.

Sara flushed scarlet. Until now Gwen had been too busy concentrating on colour schemes to question her very closely about her job, and Sara hadn't been keen to talk about it. Now she wished she had as she suspected it would seem she had deliberately kept the information from Gwen thus giving it an unnecessary touch of drama. But after all, she would be gone next day, so she might as well confess. 'I am,' she said slowly.

'You are!' Gwen's voice rose with astonishment as her eyes rounded on Sara's embarrassed face. 'Whew, darling, I'd never have guessed! Wait until I get back to the office!'

'Please, Gwen,' Sara felt forced to almost beg, 'I'd rather you didn't say anything. You see, I was secretary to the man who owned the firm before Astro's took over. I'm merely staying on for a few weeks until Mr Fenwick gets properly fixed up.'

'Oh, I see.' Gwen, looking distinctly deflated, promised not to tell, at least for the time being. Which, while sounding ambiguous, was the best, Sara realised, she might get out of her.

Sara frowned but managed to divert further curiosity by asking about Gwen's husband, a topic which fortunately absorbed Gwen above all others!

The next morning the train was crowded and Sara felt distinctly battered long before she reached the office. She had no time to return to the hotel to change and to her dismay Gwen hadn't been able to find her iron. Consequently the creases still clung to Sara's navy skirt and she was unable to do anything about it.

The letters on her desk seemed to amount to nothing more than one morning's mail, which surely conveyed that Mr Hargreaves' secretary had been busy. It was just after nine but everything was in order and, apart from a few surprised nods from the staff, no one appeared to have noticed that Sara had been away. Possibly, she thought wearily, no one might have noticed if she'd never come back.

Her own office was deserted and so was Mark's, nor was there any sign of his recent occupation. Sara went to the small cloakroom, where she left her coat and tried to make herself look tidier. Secretly she wondered if five days decorating had been wise. Not only, she was discovering, had it tired her mentally, she felt tired all over.

Returning from the cloakroom she leant against her desk, smothering a huge yawn—but not in time! The door of the inner office opened to reveal Mark. How on earth had he got there? Yet shock didn't prevent her blue eyes going huge, or her gaze from clinging, as if hungry for the sight of him.

Illogically, when she found sufficient breath, she stammered, 'How did you—I mean, when did you come in?'

'At about the usual time,' he replied silkily, his voice having a steely ring she didn't like. He continued coolly, 'Would it be presumptuous to enquire if you're here to stay or are you merely looking in?'

It was worse than she'd expected. There was no mistaking his hard sarcasm, the frightening way his dark, smouldering eyes bored into hers. Sara drew a deeply steadying breath. She wasn't going to apologise—not to him! She scarcely understood how beneath his hard stare she quivered and was barely able to speak. Swiftly she tried to pull herself together, not caring for what his threatening attitude did to her.

'There's no need to go on like this,' she muttered, hardly realising what she was saying. 'I was perfectly entitled to the days I took off. I——'

Her next words were choked off when, as if suddenly losing his temper, he reached out and jerked her roughly to him. His eyes darkened to such a harsh fury she shrank wildly away from him, certain he was about to slap her.

His grip tightened painfully. 'For the first time in my life,' he exclaimed savagely, 'I've been tempted to do a woman physical injury! But that wouldn't be the answer.' He dropped his hands from her thin shoulders and moved away, as if feeling it immediately necessary to put a little distance between them. When he turned back he was in control again, but his temper didn't seem to have subsided completely. 'Didn't you ever wonder how I was to manage without a secretary while you've been gadding around London? You come back looking as if you'd been sleeping out in one of the parks. From your air of exhaustion I'd say you've been doing just that—and with company!'

Sara was shaking so much she couldn't stop, finding the dark anger in his face frightening. She was too distracted even to think sensibly. 'No doubt you and Miss Juarez have more civilised ways of going on! Oh, I know,' she rushed on, as he seemed about to resort to violence again, 'I'm not to mention her, but is there any reason why I can't sling a little mud? You're certainly throwing plenty!'

He said curtly, to her surprise, and unconscious relief, seeming to calm down a little, 'I was worried about you, not Miss Juarez. I didn't know where you were, what you were doing.'

Bemused, Sara stared up at him. He needn't surely pretend he had been worried about herself. Or it was perhaps simply that he concerned himself over all his staff, especially when it directly affected his convenience? She paused mutinously, then was astonished to hear herself confessing, 'I was helping Gwen—you know, from Accounts, a girl I used to be friendly with. She's been married while I've been away and I was simply helping her to decorate her flat. Her husband is in the navy and she wants it finished before he gets back.'

'I see.' Clearly, although apparently willing to be more tolerant, he wasn't altogether appeased, but he merely sighed and said roughly, his eyes roaming her too-slim figure, 'If you'd stayed away longer there might not have been much of you to come back. I don't want you doing that kind of thing again. What time did you get in?'

'Only this morning.'

She felt a quick fury in him, but he merely said, 'Well, Miss Shaw, you'd better make a start right away. There's more than enough to keep us busy.'

Sara could never actually recall much of that day. She found it difficult to concentrate on anything and wasn't surprised when Mark complained several times over mistakes.

'It's certainly very obvious,' he remarked sarcastically, 'your holiday hasn't done you much good. As it's about five I suggest you leave early and try to recuperate. In any case I don't think I can stand seeing much more of you in that crumpled blouse. And for once just try to do as I say, Miss Shaw, without arguing!'

To Sara's delight she found, on reaching the hotel, that her aunt and uncle had also returned from their brief break and she spent half an hour talking to them. When she left them she suddenly remembered she would be expected to resume her normal duties, even make up for the time she had been away! She almost groaned when she met Claude in the foyer and he asked if she would go on reception at six o'clock.

'I'll try,' she promised ruefully.

In her room she was glad to get out of her creased clothes and put on a light wrapper, prior to bathing. It was unfortunate that while relaxing for a few minutes on her bed she fell asleep. It was almost seven when she woke to hear Claude banging on her door. 'Are you there, Sara?' he called. 'Is anything wrong?'

Still half asleep, she tumbled off the bed in dismay. Going to the door, she quickly wrenched it open to find Claude looking most upset. 'Oh, dear!' she exclaimed, in dazed horror, 'what time is it?'

'Nearly seven, love,' he smiled with relief at her appearance. 'I've just discovered you hadn't turned up and it's so unlike you I thought you must be ill, or perhaps had an accident? Papa sent me up here post haste.'

'Oh, gosh, I am sorry, Claude,' Sara tried to pull herself together as he entered the room, 'I didn't mean to fall asleep, but I seem to have had the most dreadful week, or day, I'm not sure which.' Suddenly, to her horror, she burst into tears.

'Sara!' His brow creasing with surprised consternation, Claude was at her side immediately, gathering her into his arms. 'What is the matter? This isn't like you, my pet! Come on, tell old Claude.'

Claude was dear and familiar and Sara clung to him miserably, knowing she couldn't tell him everything but unable to prevent herself from confessing something of what troubled her. The weight of her despair was such that it seemed impossible to keep silent. After a very short time Claude could not help being aware that she cared for a man, although she didn't say whom, but her love was not returned.

'Hush, dear,' he said softly, his hand gently touching her shining hair. 'Things are rarely as bad as one tends to think. I promise you'll be happy, if only . . .'

'Excuse me, won't you!' Mark Fenwick's hard voice startled them from the doorway. 'I don't wish to intrude.'

Sara wrenched herself from Claude's protective arms, unconscious of the tear stains still on her white cheeks. Mark here, and staring at her as if she was a stranger! Her tears gone, she had a peculiar desire to burst into hysterical giggles. If Mark's opinion of her had been low, it seemed it could get even lower, if the expression in his eyes was any-ing to judge by.

'It's me who must be excused, I'm afraid,' Claude's gaze went, suddenly comprehendingly, from one to the other. 'Duty calls, unfortunately. See you later, darling.'

As Claude departed Mark's face hardened. He glanced at Sara, Claude's 'darling' hanging like a flame between them. 'There was no need for him to go,' he said coldly. 'What I have to say won't take a minute. I merely came to tell you of a decision I made after you left the office. I'm releasing you from your position as my secretary as from the end of this week. It was what you wanted, I believe. I've already arranged with someone to take over.'

'Mark——' Sara paused, aghast, trying to find breath to continue.

Mark went on as if she had never spoken, 'This hasn't turned out exactly as I'd planned, but you will be happy at least. You'll be able to concentrate on your—er—interests here.' Ignoring the frightened paleness of her face, he walked to the door. 'I expect to see you tomorrow, of course, as usual.'

Until she reached the office next morning, Sara felt she was moving in a trance. She had since Mark had left her the evening before. She had gone down to do an hour's work for her uncle as she had promised, but her strained face had alarmed him so much he had sent her straight back to bed, sending hot milk and refreshments after her later.

At the office she was relieved to find Mark had already been in but had gone out again. It seemed he wouldn't be back until later in the day when he asked her to be ready to accompany him on a matter of some importance. This was all he said in his brief, written message and she had no idea what it was about.

She was ready about three, as he requested, wishing fer-vently, as it was Friday, that she might have been spared this final ordeal, but quite composed. Inside she felt so dead she didn't think she could have worried over anything. With a folder clutched in her hand against her handbag, and looking neatly attractive in a fresh, flowered cotton dress, she ran down to where Mark waited below in his car.

Getting into the highly powered limousine, she was surprised Mark hadn't brought his driver. She wished he had as a third party, however detached, might have lightened the atmosphere.

They left Coventry on the A423, Sara, as yet, having no clear idea where she was going. Nor did she like to ask as Mark seemed far from communicative. They passed Southam, an old market town with a bridge over the river Itchen, then after several more miles, Oxford, the area around here being too dearly familiar for Sara to view with much equanimity. After this, because she was still tired, she allowed her thoughts to wander nostalgically into the past and eventually fell asleep. When her eyes opened again, to her astonishment, they were bumping down the rutted track which led to Mark's cottage.

'Why are we going here?' Struggling to a more upright position, she tried to speak normally, but unfortunately her query came out in a hoarse whisper.

'Wait and see,' Mark replied curtly, his glance sliding narrowly to her startled, tormented face.

Sara drew a quick breath, refusing to look at him as she subsided. It couldn't really matter, it was no use getting in a state about something long since past. Mark must merely be stopping to check something or pick something up, and it would certainly not be a memory.

Stopping in front of the cottage, he moved immediately around to her side, holding open the door until she got out. 'You may as well come in,' he countered her dazed glance, 'I may be some time.'

'As you wish,' she shrugged, trying hard not to appear shaken. Never must he guess she would have given anything to have been able to stay in the car.

He took her arm, his demeanour as apparently careless as her tones as he guided her up the short path. Once inside he abruptly let her go and closed the door, leaving her standing anxiously in the hall while he disappeared into the lounge.

The hall was warm with late spring sunshine and, as she waited in the gentle silence, there came the unmistakable surprising crackle of wood. Surely Mark could not be lighting fires? How long did he intend staying?

The smell of burning wood began to filter aromatically through the open doorway, but a few minutes later, when Mark came back, Sara still hadn't moved. 'Aren't you coming any further?' he mocked, standing to one side as if to emphasise his meaning.

'I'd rather not, Mark!' Before she could stop it the panic she had tried to control took over. There seemed nothing she could do about it. Feverishly her voice rose as her eyes darkened with visible pain. 'Please, Mark,' she begged, 'I don't want to stay here. Please don't make me!'

For a long moment he said nothing as they remained staring at each other, the air taut with electricity between them. Then suddenly he had reached her in one stride and was pulling her fiercely into his arms. 'Sara,' he muttered roughly, 'Sara, my darling, don't you know how much I want you?'

He had left his jacket, which he had removed for driving, in the back of the car, and she could feel the hard muscles of his chest through his shirt against her breasts as he strained her to him. 'Do you love me?' he asked, his lips moving on hers.

'Yes.' She was somehow past pretence, past caring that he might not love her, or what he thought. 'Yes, Mark, I do love you,' she whispered, the relief of being able to say so at last made her want to repeat it again and again. 'You don't know how much!' she sobbed, torn between happiness and tears.

'Sara!' He was instantly quieting and comforting, lifting her swiftly into his arms. He carried her into the lounge, still holding her close, as if she was too precious to release even for a second. 'I'm sorry,' he murmured against her damp cheek, 'if I've been a brute. You might not understand, but I didn't know what to do for the best. I had to try to be fair to you, you were so very young, my love.'

'I've not felt that young for a long time,' she quivered, burying her hot face in his neck. He hadn't yet said that he loved her, but somehow she was content to hope, to wait. The strength of his arms instinctively reassured her, but first, it seemed, she must convince him she was old enough to know her own mind. In his eyes there was still a degree of doubt.

'Mark——' she began, but before she could go on his hand went with hard purpose under her chin, turning her lips to his. As his mouth came down on hers the world faded and she felt within her the familiar melting sensation of her bones turning to water, of her senses stirring dizzily beneath his passionate expertise.

'Darling,' she murmured illogically, when much later her mouth was freed, as his trailed elsewhere, 'why did you bring me here today?'

'Because I believed it was the only place where we wouldn't be interrupted,' he said grimly, his lips softly exploring her face. 'Ever since I came to Coventry it's seemed almost impossible to get you completely to myself, not without something or someone coming between us. I decided this cottage was the only answer.'

'But last night you were so—horrid!'

'Last night, my dear, I felt horrid! Until after I'd talked with your uncle.'

'Uncle René?'

'Yes,' Mark reiterated mockingly, 'Uncle René! But before we go into that, Sara, I think we should go back to the beginning.'

It was so wonderful to be here in Mark's arms, she would have settled for this without further talk. Sensing it was important to him she gave in, but not without cost. Even to think of the beginning made her face go pale, her slender body taut.

'Sara,' his eyes were compassionate on her distraught face but his mouth was firm, 'you know it's the only way or I wouldn't have suggested it. I, too, can think of other things I'd rather do. After we've solved all our problems I intend kissing you until you beg for mercy.'

Sara felt high colour mount her cheeks at this. 'Mark Fenwick——' she began, but he merely shushed her.

'I remember,' he said slowly, holding her close, his gaze sombre, 'how I felt when I first saw you. My heart has never been the same since.'

'I thought I irritated you beyond everything?'

'You did, my darling. That is, I tried to believe you did, but I'm afraid not even then was I prepared to let you go. Do you think I would have allowed such a situation to develop over a small, unimportant-looking handbag if I hadn't been attracted? I tried to convince myself it was a case of one thing leading to another, but I was perfectly aware this wasn't altogether true.'

'Then you brought me here, that first time,' she said, in a trembling voice.

'Sara!' his breathing deepened as his hand slid caressingly over her slender shoulder, 'you don't know what I went through that night. I hadn't really believed anyone could be so innocent. I hadn't allowed for it, or for the powerful feelings you suddenly aroused in me. I'd never been in love before, you see, and even then, with you in my arms, I wasn't prepared to admit it. I only let myself believe furiously that you'd tricked me. I remember when I left you at your hostel the next day I was racked with an insane desire to haul you straight back into my car and drive straight to the nearest register office and demand we be married.' A faint smile touched Mark's lips as he paused. 'I don't know how I was to have managed it, but somehow I should have persuaded someone.'

'But you didn't.' Sara had no idea how desolate she sounded.

'No,' he sighed grimly. 'Instead I spent a hell of a week —and I really mean that—abroad. Coming back I had every intention of talking seriously about the future. You were so young I was plagued with doubts, but at the same time, I couldn't leave you. The coincidence of finding you with Richard was almost too much. It seemed to emphasise your apparent immaturity, a too youthful tendency to flit from one man to another.'

'Mark!' Sara's face was strained, 'you didn't actually think that, did you?'

'I think I did, then,' he confessed. 'Later, when I got the truth out of Richard, I realised how wrong I'd been. He'd had an idea my sister would come up to Town that evening. Their marriage had been on the rocks for some time, only the new lady in my dear brother-in-law's life hadn't wanted to be involved in divorce proceedings, if you follow me. To them both it seemed much easier to let some other girl provoke my sister into starting a divorce. Unfortunately this happened to be you.'

Sara shuddered, such deception being beyond her. She found it almost impossible to believe someone like Dicky could have contrived it.

'Better to forget it, my love,' Mark advised, as if he read her mind. 'He got his divorce eventually, but not through you. The whole affair did leave me even more doubtful about marriage, though. It seemed you must be given time to grow up and meet other men.'

'So you let me go?' Sara's eyes were bleak as she recalled what seemed to her years of unnecessary suffering.

'Yes,' he agreed heavily, 'I came to the conclusion that I had no alternative but to do so. To go on seeing you without marrying you could, I believed, only lead to one thing, and I didn't want that for you. It was a temptation I felt forced to put from me.'

'But after three years, Mark,' her voice broke. 'Why did

you leave it so long? Isn't it too late?'

'I hope not, darling.' His mouth came down, momentarily hard on the softness of hers. 'I know it's been a long time, but I knew where you were, if not exactly what you were doing. I deliberately made myself wait to give you a chance of making a new life of your own if you wanted to, and you're still extremely young. Actually this Coventry deal took longer to pull off than I expected—it's over a year since we began the initial enquiries. Besides, you never once tried to contact me?'

'How could I, Mark?'

'All the young women I've known could have done so very easily,' he grinned. 'I'm afraid cynicism dies hard in a man.'

She said gently, decided to overlook that, 'But you did come at last.'

'Yes. I didn't dare hope the excellent Miss Shaw that George Dent mentioned could be you. When I discovered it was I thought most of my troubles must be over, but it wasn't to be as easy as that.'

'I was frightened of being hurt again,' Sara whispered. 'I also soon had the impression you were involved with Miss Juarez. When she followed you to London on your orders, at least I overheard her saying she'd come immediately she received your message, I thought I should die. Before she arrived it had been bad enough because I couldn't relax, afterwards it was terrible.'

'Sara, child,' he held her, kissing her deeply, 'so that was the trouble? If I'd thought for a moment you'd heard! I never sent for Dolores, that was her own idea, I merely left a message saying I would be out of town. It was simply a calculated guess on her part as to where I would be. Unfortunately I had to play along with her. My chairman, you see, is busy negotiating with her father over some shares he very much wants, and he asked me not to do anything to upset Dolores. Actually Dolores and I have known each other for years and have never had anything remotely like an affair. Certainly I've never loved her, and she knows it.'

Sara couldn't stop a surge of relief from flooding through her as he spoke, although she suspected Dolores might have cared for him more than he realised. Yet in spite of a new, intense happiness she couldn't help saying, 'When you sent me away last week, I thought you didn't care for me either.'

'Because, my love, I'd decided if you couldn't trust me after all this time there could be no future for us.'

'But you also, I think, were suspicious of my cousin Claude. Poor Claude, how he would laugh, I'm afraid, if I were to tell him, especially as he's already engaged to an extremely sweet girl.'

'So I was no better.' Ruefully Mark smoothed the heavy hair from off Sara's hot forehead. 'I didn't know he was your cousin and that the hotel belongs to your uncle. Not until your uncle talked to me this morning and acquainted me with a lot of things I didn't know about you. Some things,' he added, with some severity, 'you should have told me yourself.'

She smiled faintly. 'You were never very curious. You could have shown more interest.'

'Perhaps I was afraid to, but I will in future. I'm going to be a jealous husband, my darling, so be warned. When we're married——'

Sara interrupted. 'Mark, you haven't asked me yet!'

His eyes softened as he saw her dazed expression, but the humour left his face as he tilted up her chin and his lips found hers, bruising her tender mouth fiercely. He said thickly against her lips, 'I love you more than life itself, Sara, but you aren't the only one whose head is whirling. I certainly told your uncle I wanted to marry you, and I hope you'll agree?'

'Oh, yes, Mark darling!' Without words her radiant face would have been answer enough and his mouth descended again, his hands hard and searching on her soft body.

Later he murmured, 'Am I hurting you?'

She shook her head, making no attempt to free herself,

but slid her hands under his shirt. He held her tightly, caressing her until he felt her surrendering to the hot tide of passion he aroused in her. 'Mark,' she whispered, 'I love you.'

'Darling,' his lips moved against her closed eyes, 'it's getting late. I'd like to stay here all night, but I've waited all these years. I think I can wait a few more days.'

With an effort she looked at him, her face paling. 'If you asked me I don't think I could refuse.'

'I know, my love,' he put her gently from him, his eyes smouldering, 'but I don't want you to have any regrets. I'll make some coffee and we'll have it in front of the fire before we go.'

'As you wish ...'

'Not as I wish, Sara,' he replied, his voice low but leaving her in no doubt he was in command and would be strong for her as well as himself. 'How would you like to spend part of your honeymoon here—the first part?'

Anywhere with Mark, she felt, would have been paradise, but at the cottage it would be especially so! Happily she agreed.

'Afterwards,' he went on, 'I'll take you to an island I know off the coast of Greece. There's practically only the sea and sun, but for our honeymoon this should be sufficent.' With mock severity he added, 'I don't want you interested in anything or anyone but me, not for the next month or two at the least!'

'A typically selfish male!'

'I intend to remain so, as far as you're concerned, my beautiful Sara.'

Sara gazed at him, her heart in her eyes as, unable to resist the temptation, he pulled her close. She would never mind what she did or where she went again as long as she was by his side. 'I love you, Mark,' she whispered, 'I've loved you since the very beginning.' With a small sigh she closed her eyes and clung to him as their lips met.

Harlequin's
Collection
EDITIONS OF 1979

YESTERDAY'S LOVE
FOR ALL YOUR TOMORROWS

You relive your love in memories. Letters tied in blue
ribbon...roses pressed between the pages of a book...
keepsakes of a romance that will never be forgotten.

A great love story has a different kind of timelessness.
It can be cherished in memory, but it can also come
alive over and over again. Harlequin proved that
three years ago, when we introduced the first 100
Collections—outstanding novels, chosen from two
decades of beautiful love stories. Stories that are still
treasured by the women who read them.

Now we are bringing you the
Harlequin's Collection
editions of 1979. Best-selling
romantic novels that were
written from the heart, giving
them a brilliance that the
passage of time cannot dim.
Like a lovingly crafted family
heirloom or a gift from
someone you love, these
stories will have a special
personal significance.
Because when you read
them today, you'll relive
love. A love that will last,
for all your tomorrows.

$1.25 each

Choose from this list of classic Collection editions

Relive a great romance...
Harlequin's Collection 1979
Complete and mail this coupon today!

Harlequin Reader Service

In U.S.A.
MPO Box 707
Niagara Falls, N.Y. 14302

In Canada
649 Ontario St.
Stratford, Ontario, N5A 6W2

Please send me the following Harlequin's Collection novels. I am enclosing my check or money order for $1.25 for each novel ordered, plus 49¢ to cover postage and handling.

☐ 152	☐ 161	☐ 169
☐ 153	☐ 162	☐ 170
☐ 154	☐ 163	☐ 171
☐ 155	☐ 164	☐ 172
☐ 156	☐ 165	☐ 173
☐ 158	☐ 166	☐ 174
☐ 159	☐ 167	☐ 175
☐ 160	☐ 168	☐ 176

Number of novels checked @ $1.25 each = $ _____

N.Y and N.J. residents add appropriate sales tax $ _____

Postage and handling $ _____ .49

                              TOTAL $ _____

NAME_____
(Please Print)

ADDRESS _____

CITY _____

STATE/PROV. _____

ZIP/POSTAL CODE_____

Offer expires December 31, 1979   ROM 2284

Harlequin
Presents...

The beauty of true romance...
The excitement of world travel...

unique love stories for today's woman

Harlequin Presents...
novels of honest,
twentieth-century love,
with characters who
are interesting, vibrant
and alive.

The elegance of love...
The warmth of romance...
The lure of faraway places...

Six new novels, every
month — wherever
paperbacks are sold.

JOY
ROMANCE
LOVE

Harlequin Omnibus

THREE love stories in ONE beautiful volume

The joys of being in love...
the wonder of romance...
the happiness that true love brings...

Now yours in the HARLEQUIN OMNIBUS edition every month wherever paperbacks are sold.